# SCENES FROM AN INDIAN SUMMER

## JOHN FOGARTY

First published 2015 by

Wordsonthestreet

Six San Antonio Park, Salthill, Galway, Ireland
www.wordsonthestreet.com
publisher@wordsonthestreet.com

The moral right of the author has been asserted.

A catalogue record for this book is available from the British Library.

ISBN 978-1-907017-38-4

Cover design, layout and typesetting: Wordsonthestreet
Printed and bound in the UK

# SCENES FROM AN INDIAN SUMMER

## ABOUT THE AUTHOR

John Fogarty lives in Fethard, Co. Tipperary. He has had work published in a range of publications at home and abroad.

He is also an actor and has taken roles in numerous productions, most notably in JB Priestley's *An Inspector Calls* and in Reginald Rose's *Twelve Angry Men*.

He returned to education in 2002 and graduated from the University of Limerick in 2007 with a first class honours degree in English Literature.

To Joey and Leish
We feel your absence

# Contents

*Alas, the summer's energy wanes quickly, a moment and it is gone.*

John Ashbery, from *Soonest Mended.*

# Prologue

# Winter Dreaming

'When we get the summer holidays we'll build an Indian camp,' Paudie said.

'Yeah, with teepees, real teepees,' said Jim.

'Like the Apaches,' Paudie said.

'We can draw poles from the wood,' said Jim.

I tried to think of something to add, wanting to be as good as them.

'We can all be Indians, I mean like, we can all call ourselves after an Indian, you know, like, Paudie you could be Crazy Horse.'

'Shaggin Crazy Horse, feck's sake, Jonno, are you making out I'm crazy?'

'Naw, Crazy Horse wasn't *crazy*, he was, you know, one of the top Indian chiefs.'

'Taking Indian names – that's stupid,' Paudie said.

'Snot,' I said.

Paudie was only saying it was stupid because I'd thought of it, not him.

Jim folded his arms, crossed his legs, sat upright, lengthened his face.

'Me big Chief Sitting Bull,' he said.

'Him Big Chief *Shitting* Bull,' Paudie screeched.

We laughed.

And forgot for a moment the fire in our fingers and the biting breeze from the east.

'Hey, c'mon will ye, them spuds won't sow themselves,' the father called.

We were helping him sow potatoes in the plot that the Council had given us in a field behind our house.

The Poor Man's Plot.

That was Paddy Harney's name for it.

It was March and impossible to keep warm in the bitter east wind that numbed our fingers, coloured our bare legs shades of purple. Bit into the rims of our ears.

Every day on the radio in our kitchen Cliff Richard was singing about going on a summer holiday, going where the sun shines brightly, going where the sea is blue. Making me feel vaguely dissatisfied. Long for blue skies that were permanent, wouldn't disappear in a matter of minutes.

And there we were crouched for shelter against the stone boundary wall between the plots and Cummins' field. I'd zipped the corduroy jerkin that I'd got in a parcel from England all the way to my throat, turned the collar up. I loved that jerkin, not minding that it was an English cousin's cast-off. But it couldn't keep that east wind out. My shoes were splitting apart and caked in the dung that the father had spread in the furrows. I longed for the potato planting to be over, for the east wind to be gone. To be able to go inside, to the kitchen, where the mother would have a warm fire glowing. Press the old overcoat tightly to the butt of the east-facing front door. Keep that biting breeze out.

Let it whistle in the chimney while I sat in to the heat. Dreaming of summertime instead. Of the long holidays. Of sunny Sunday afternoons, Indian camps, listening to *Pick of the Pops* on the tranny Judo's aul' fella had brought from London. Of things we'd do when sunny days were here. If they ever were.

Dream of Apaches, baking deserts, bows and arrows.

'C'mon will ye,' the father shouted.

We stood up into the east wind.

Summer a dream in the distance.

# 1

# Breaking Loose

As soon as the bell went at lunchtime and the prayer was said we were off. Folding desk seats slamming up, timber clattering on timber, feet pounding, dust rising from wooden floorboards.

Brother Virgilius, in his black soutane and green sash, gazed sourly at us from behind his desk. Waiting for us to be gone. Wishing, probably, that we would never come back. That some Pied Piper would lead us away forever into a cave in the foothills of Sliabhnamon, like the children of Hamelin never to be seen again. Or that he might be sent to some well off school where there were no runny noses, no lice-ridden hair. No squint-eyed, cross-eyed, bug-eyed, lazy-eyed, stye-eyed children. No big red boils swelling on the backs of necks. No smelly, patched clothes, frayed shirt collars. No scabby knees.

I didn't care about him, though, left him sitting there sour and solitary, heedless of whatever inner agonies he may have been enduring.

The forty or so of us boys from fifth and sixth class stampeded towards the door and freedom, crowding and crushing in the musty air of the small porch outside the classroom door. The boys from third and fourth pushing into the porch too. Being forced to give way to us, the bigger lads. The thick smell of fart and greasy clothes. A bedlam of voices as we burst out into summer, glorious summer, with all its pleasures waiting on us. Running, running, almost airborne with excitement.

Across the schoolyard.

Bags on backs.

Breaking loose.

Running carefree into the long summer of freedom that stretched before us to infinity, all lengthy days and short nights.

This bursting out of the classroom at lunchtime usually

developed into a race to the arch that in the long ago had been the northern gate into the old town.

But it was different that summer day of June 1963. It was the last day of school, I was elated, free, free, didn't care who won the race to the arch.

As soon as I passed under the archway that was it, the end – no more school. I wouldn't walk under it again until September. And that seemed a lifetime away.

I turned into the Back Lane at a leisurely pace. Skirting round the spot where some drunk had squatted with urgency the night before on his way home.

In no hurry now.

Time my hoard.

'Lincoln Vail of the Everglades, the man on patrol in the Everglades.'

Someone was singing behind me. The theme song from *The Everglades*, a TV show that we watched on Mamie Mackey's telly. Across her half-door.

'Hey, hey wait, hold on willya.'

It was Judo. Still with his blonde crew cut, even though everybody was trying to let their hair grow long, because of the Beatles and all those Merseybeat groups from Liverpool.

The father always made sure, though, that none of us had long hair.

'By Jaysus, there won't be any of ye going around this town looking like shaggin potes,' he'd say, running his hair machine from the base of our skulls to the crown until a crooked fringe was all that remained of our lengthening locks.

I truly hated the cold feel of that hair machine on my skull as it ripped my dreams away. And tiny chunks of my scalp.

'When are ya going to let the hair grow, Judo?' I asked.

'When the aul' fella kicks the bucket, I suppose,' he answered.

'Look,' he said, elbowing me, pointing.

Rachel Horan was at her door. Perky as an angry black sparrow. Eyes flitting left, right, all around. Shaking bread crumbs from the folds of her apron. All in black with a kind of shawl

14

round her shoulders fastened crosswise over her scrawny front. Her hens darted after the crumbs. They were always clucking and scratching about in the laneway. She shot us a warning look through her little round spectacles.

'Mind them hens now let ye, touch them hens me boyos and yeer in big trouble,' she said.

If she hadn't been there we'd have sent them flapping and squawking around the laneway.

I glanced at her, keeping the width of the lane between us, fearing she might launch an attack with her broom which she could suddenly produce from nowhere.

Rachel Horan, the fastest broomstick in the West.

Faster than Billy the Kid.

Just then our Paudie and Jim, along with the Horse, came charging off the Rocklow road into the Back Lane.

'Chook, chook, chook, chook, chook!' they shouted, sending Rachel's hens flapping and squawking.

She came rushing out the door waving her broom.

'Ye feckin whelps, ye little blackguards, I'll get the guards onto ye so I will.'

We ran, Judo and I, along with the others.

We stopped where the Back Lane met the Main Street. Looked back. There she was, standing opposite the back window of the slaughterhouse, waving the broom, shouting at us.

'The divil fire ye anyway, I know who ye are so I do, don't worry, I'll have the sergeant onto ye, so I will, and the parish priest, and yeer fathers, and yeer mothers.'

We ran on, executing a rapid sign of the cross and a jerk of the right knee as we passed the church. Brother Ultan had told us once that we should genuflect and bless ourselves when passing the church because of the Real Presence inside in the tabernacle.

'Hey, look,' said Paudie, pointing at the window of Jack Moore's clothes shop.

Wellingtons, boots, overalls, donkey jackets, were arranged haphazardly in the window. Dark, heavy trousers, the kind that farmers wore. Farmers smelling of cattle would step into Jack's

15

on their way home from the mart on Saturdays, stand awkwardly in the shop, examine the work-wear cautiously, lengthily, forever reluctant to part with money.

We stopped.

I squinted through the plate glass into the dim interior.

Jack was behind the counter studying a pile of invoices through glasses balanced on the tip of his nose, stroking a face that always looked cold and cadaverous even on the hottest summer day. A pair of waders hanging from a hook on the ceiling moved fractionally just above his head.

The big window in Jack's clothes shop was protected by a round, tubular bar, fixed to the wall and the footpath. It was about three feet above the pavement. Meant to keep cattle from arsing into the window on fair day Tuesdays. We sprung onto it, balancing on our stomachs for a split second before doing a quick twirl, head first, over and under the bar to land back on the footpath. Jack hated us doing that. We loved and feared his reaction. This time my heels struck the window on the way round making the glass rattle, bringing Jack to the door in a fury, face contorted. Gathering ourselves in an ecstasy of terror and excitement we took flight across the Convent bridge. Knowing he couldn't follow and leave the shop unattended we stopped when we'd reached the other side. Jack was at the Convent gate, shaking his fist, scowling at us.

'Feckin bostoons,' he shouted.

That's what he always called us. Bostoons.

He shouted after us again.

'A right shower o' bostoons, that's what ye are.'

'Jaysus, did ya see the aul' puss on him?' Paudie said, gasping and laughing.

We began jumping up and down off the low wall outside the cinema. *Apache Territory,* the billboard to the left of the front door proclaimed in blood-red lettering. There was that to look forward to on Sunday afternoon. If we could scrape the money together.

'I'm getting the Judy first,' Paudie shouted, suddenly racing off.

We chased after him. He got there first, was pushed aside by Horse, recovered, jumped on Horse's back and wrestled him to the ground. Jim jumped in, turned the tap on, half blocked the spout with two fingers spraying water in a wide arc across the road. Judo and I stayed just beyond the reach of the spray, taunting him, advancing when the stream weakened as Jim's fingers tired, retreating when he found the range again. Squealing and shouting until Peggie Hanley came from her house across the street. Teetering on high heels.

'G'wan home outa that ye little feckers before I get the sergeant onto ye,' she shouted.

'Ah, we're sorry, Peggie, we're sorry, don't tell the aul' sergeant,' Paudie called back.

'Yeah,' said Judo, 'don't tell Lincoln Vail, Peggie, please.'

'Lincoln Vail me arse, who the feckin hell is Lincoln Vail?' Peggie snorted.

'The man on patrol in The Everglades,' we all sang out together.

'Mind yeer cheek now, bounce off home with yeerselves now to whoever owns ye,' she answered.

Paddy Heffernan had appeared at the door of his bicycle shed, was taking stock.

'Them young lads won't lave us a drop o' water, so they won't,' he called to Peggie.

We picked our wet schoolbags off the ground and headed past the cinema and across The Valley.

John Lacey was standing in his doorway smoking a Gold Flake. Staring intently at us as we passed.

'Seeya after,' Judo shouted as he ran down the road to his own house.

A few minutes later we were in the low light of our kitchen.

'Yeer home,' the mother said.

# 2

# The Mother

The mother was always in the kitchen when we got back to the house. No matter where we'd been. No matter how long we'd been away. Whether we were coming from school or back from a day's gallivanting – there she'd be. Waiting for us, always waiting. And if she wasn't waiting for us she'd be waiting for the father. And we just expected her to be there all the time, immovable and changeless as Sliabhnamon.

Coming from school that day we charged into the kitchen, laughing, shouldering one another. Throwing our schoolbags under the bed. Right to the farthest, darkest corner.

'Quit that caffling, let ye,' she said.

She was at the table, putting a cross on a cake of brown bread before sliding it into the oven of the new gas cooker that she'd bought on hire purchase. It had fascinated us at first, with its red knobs and instant blue flame. Mamie Mackey and Ellie Power had come in to see it in action. Sometimes, though, the weekly payments couldn't be met and the Monday man in his wrinkled suit had to be fobbed off by one of us as the mother stood away from the door and window anxiously listening.

Two more cakes were cooling on the sill of the open window. The smell of baking swirled sweetly around her like incense. The heat from the oven had put a flush on her pale face. She brushed at a strand of hair with floury fingers.

'Ssh, keep quiet now, let ye,' she said.

She was listening to Kennedy on the radio. This was the third day of his visit and he was giving a big speech somewhere. He was glamourous and good looking with unbelievably white teeth, like a film star. That's what he seemed like to me: a film star. An Irish film star. Because we thought of him as Irish. But not a Barry Fitzgerald, leprechauny kind of Irish. Nor a tough, two-fisted

James Cagney kind of Irish. No, he was a hero.

Brother Virgilius had been telling us all about him. How he was really Irish. And a war hero.

Like Audie Murphy, I'd thought.

Virgy had even made us learn part of his speech, the one that went ask not what your country can do for you and all that kinda stuff. I felt a shiver run through me every time I heard those words. They sounded like something from the Parables that we were learning at school.

There was a small bust of Kennedy on the mantelpiece in our kitchen and just above him, a picture of a smiling Pope John XXIII. The mother had bought that picture from a door-to-door pedlar when the sour-looking Pope who was there before him had died and he'd been elected the new Pope.

On the radio Kennedy was talking about the Irish who'd fought in battles in the American Civil war. And the way he talked, you just had to listen.

He named some of the battles: Fredericksburg, Martha's Farm, Allen's Hill.

I pictured all the brave soldiers marching under flags and banners in their neat blue uniforms.

They were the fighting Irish, I thought, heart swelling with pride.

The mother was listening, transfixed, carried away by Kennedy's speech.

'Mam, I want me lunch,' Jim said.

'Will ye whisht, will ye, ye'll get it in a minute, when he's finished talking,' she said.

'I'm hungry, Mam,' Jim said.

'Wait, I said.'

'But we're going to the wood today Mam, with the lads in the gang, we're getting poles for our Indian camp, we have to hurry on or they won't wait for us.'

Kennedy went on for a bit longer. He spoke about the bravery of the Irish, the Fighting 69th he called them, and that name rang out gloriously and it seemed to me that the Irish were the bravest

and greatest soldiers of all. Their flag had been riddled with
bullets at Fredericksburg, he said. And it all sounded so noble and
courageous that I longed to have been out there with them,
getting myself riddled like that flag, becoming a great Irish hero in
the cause of freedom. I didn't know what the cause of freedom
was but it sounded like something really worth dying for.

When he'd finished the mother began slicing and buttering
bread.

'Let me tell ye here and now there won't be any gallivantin''
for ye today, not 'til that plot is sorted out. Yeer father said ye
were to weed those spuds before they're smothered altogether.'

'But Mam,' Paudie said.

'I'm telling ye now, if he comes home this evening and it's not
done, there'll be war, I'm telling ye, war.'

'Ah come on Mam, the lads are all waiting for us, down at
Horse's house,' Paudie.

'C'mon Mam, please, we'll do the weeding tomorrow,' Jim
said.

She stood there, suddenly motionless, staring. For a moment it
seemed as though she was somewhere else, somewhere distant;
her eyes were fixed on the picture of Pope John, but she was
seeing beyond that to something visible only in her mind's eye.
Sometimes she was like that when a song or a piece of music came
on the radio, especially if it was melancholy or sad, she would
gaze away, become absent. As if the music had aroused a longing
inside of her. It was scary, because it seemed as though she'd left
us for a while. Maybe even wanted to leave us, get away from us.

'Please, Mam, please,' we chorused, anxiously.

'Oh all right so,' she said then, coming back, 'but yeer to do it
first thing in the morning mind – d'ye hear me now?

We cheered.

'Oh, we will, Mammy, we will,' we shouted.

The truth was she could never be strict with us.

I was glad we were getting off. There was nothing I hated more
than weeding in the garden. Crawling up and down, up and down
between the potato stalks, stones cutting into your knees, tiny

nettles stinging the bare flesh of your legs as you pulled half-heartedly at scutch grass and weeds. Wishing you were down at the river catching brickileens or reading comics, or making a catapault or a bow and arrow maybe. Anywhere, as long as it was somewhere else, away from the drudgery and boredom of weeding. But we'd been granted a reprieve today.

As we finished our lunch of brown bread and jam the mother was setting up the zinc bath on two chairs, getting ready to wash clothes.

We gave no thought to that or her labours. We were making for the door leaving a mess of spilled tea, crusts and breadcrumbs on the table for her to clean up.

'Mind yeerselves in that wood now,' she called after us, 'and look out for that feckin gamekeeper.'

She was there, stooped over the washing board as we left, lathering the collar of a shirt.

She'd be there in the kitchen, we knew, when we arrived back hours later.

Waiting on us.

# 3

# Being Apaches

The wood at Grove wasn't far – about a mile or so from the town when you cut to it across the fields. Along Jesuits' walk, past the town dump, past Mrs. McGrath's ramshackle farmhouse, down that overgrown laneway to the Furry Hill, then the leg-stretching climb up the rocky slope of the Doctor's Hill. From there you could see the wood, spread across the face of a steep hill, covering maybe nine or ten acres. But in my imagination it was a sprawling, unexplored forest without boundaries.

It was one of my favourite places, stirring with shadows, haunted, mysterious, the chirupping of many birds mingling with the sound of water coursing downhill over stones when you were inside. Sometimes light slanted strangely from above, beaming onto masses of ferns rising from a spongy carpet of bluebell leaves. Far away amongst distant trees you'd hear mysterious sounds. Sounds that made you pause, listen nervously. Poised for flight. Wondering: is that the gamekeeper prowling along twisting pathways, or just raggedy old Simon, taking a ramble from his rundown house with the rusty iron roof on the edge of the wood?

Sometimes I imagined it was Sherwood Forest and we were Robin Hood's merry men roaming its trails and secret hideaways.

From this day on, though, until the end of summer we were going to be Indians. Apaches, my favourite Indians. They were the best trackers, could travel for miles without leaving a footprint or any sign that they'd passed that way, could run fifty miles across the deserts of Arizona without stopping for a drink of water. And they were the best horsemen of all the Indians. That's what it said in the library book I'd been reading on Indian tribes. Of course we didn't have any desert and there was plenty of water but still the Apaches were the ones we modelled ourselves on. There were photos of them in the book. The Apaches in those photos looked nothing like the ones I'd seen in films. They appeared tired, defeated, their blank faces scarified as the bark on ancient trees. Sitting on miserable, knobbly-kneed pinto ponies.

The Apaches in my imagination never looked like the ones in those photos: I always saw them as they were in the flicks. Tanned, wrinkle-free, muscular. Noble.

Sometimes though we'd fancy being Cheyenne, or Sioux. Then we'd fight over who was going to be Rain in the Face or Sitting Bull. It depended on what film we'd seen at the Capitol cinema. And after seeing *Custer's Last Stand* we were torn between Custer as he made his heroic last stand and being Sitting Bull, directing hordes of warriors to slaughter The Yellow-Hair and his white-eyes with a wave of his lance. Custer was a bit of a hero, with his long blond hair and being the last man standing at Little Big Horn surrounded by the bodies of his fallen comrades, heroically fighting off the entire Sioux nation.

Vague images absorbed from *Custer's Last Stand*, and innumerable cowboy and Indian films that I'd seen at the Capitol, were ghosting through my imagination as I ran towards Horse's house to meet the gang on that first day of the summer holidays. Lagging well behind Paudie and Jim as usual. Within three minutes of leaving our house Kennedy and working in the plot were forgotten.

'Wait for me, wait for me will ye,' I called.

They didn't.

'You're too feckin slow,' Paudie said, when I arrived, panting.

'Yah, you're useless,' Jim said.

'You better not slow us down going to the wood,' Paudie said.

The Valley Gang ran everywhere. To the wood, to the swimming hole. Going to rob orchards. The only time we didn't run was when we were going to school. Then it was the slowest of slow walks.

'I won't slow ye down, I swear, I'll keep up, I'll be ok once I get me wind,' I said.

Horse always told me that I was useless to run.

'You're feckin useless, you're broken-winded,' he'd tell me, with great contempt, as I wheezed and tried to suck in air after running hard across fields, through ditches, up hills, down hills, along roads and laneways trying to keep up.

So far this day, I'd only run a hundred yards or so. There was still a full mile to go before we reached the wood. And the upper was parting from the sole of the shoe on my left foot, making running a bit tricky. If you stubbed the flapping sole against even the smallest thing you'd go sprawling.

I didn't care though. If I had to run across a desert that day I would not have minded. The summer lay all before me, I felt free as a bird, full of excitement as I launched myself into an infinity of carefree days.

What more could I have asked for?

# 4

## To The Wood Once More

'I have me Bowie knife,' Jim said, drawing it from the scabbard that he wore on his snake belt.

He loved whipping it from the scabbard to show off his throws. He could throw it with a spin, make it stick with a thunk and a quiver in a tree or a piece of board.

'I fecked a loan of the small hatchet,' Paudie said.

I felt in my pocket, making sure my penknife was there. There was only one pocket in my summer britches that didn't have a hole. I always had to be sure I put it in that one. We were all milling around now, talking loudly, getting edgy, anxious to head off to the wood.

'Look,' Judo said, flashing his flick knife.

He was always showing it off. And he knew we all envied him because no-one else had one like it. He wouldn't even let me hold it in my own hand. His aul' fella had brought it to him from London when he'd come home for the Christmas holidays.

Must be great to have an aul' fella in London or someplace like that, I'd thought.

All the things he might bring back with the big money they got over there. I wished sometimes that our father would go to London. Send money back to us. Still, when the time came for them to go back there was always a heaviness in their step as they made their way reluctantly to the railway station.

'It's not a *real* flick knife, anyway only Teddy Boys have *real* flick knives,' Horse had said, dismissing it. Enviously.

Even though he'd never seen a real flick knife.

'C'mon Horse, when are we going?' Judo asked.

There was a chorus of 'yeahs' and 'c'mons.'

Horse glared at us.

'We'll go when I have meself ready,' he said.

Horse was checking to make sure we had tools to cut the poles in the wood. He had a small saw from a carpenter set that someone had got for Christmas thrust inside his snake belt.

25

'Right,' he said, 'remember, no more cissy stuff.'

Philly Landy and Dusty O'Brien had been sword-fighting like the Three Musketeers, using sticks as rapiers. With jam-pot lids as knuckle protectors.

'All that aul' sword-fighting shite is finished, remember we're Apache braves now,' Horse said, throwing them a dirty look.

'Yeah,' said Judo, pushing Philly, giving him a look.

'All right let's ride out,' Horse shouted, sprinting away along the road.

We followed behind, whooping and screeching, kicking our imaginary war ponies into a gallop.

Mom Mom Gunn's terrier came chasing after us for a while, yelping and barking us out of The Valley and part of the way along Jesuits' Walk. I was at the rear of the gang and wished I had a real horse that might give the bloody little effer a kick that'd crack his skull open. He was always chasing after us, snapping at our heels and trying to bite us.

There was about a dozen or so in the gang and soon we were strung out in a long line, like a wagon train: Horse at the head, Judo and I last, forming the rearguard as usual. Horse called a halt when he reached the top of the Doctor's Hill.

From there we could look across the countryside, green hills all around, soft and smooth. Market Hill to our left, Bennetshill rising in a broad sweep to our right – where Cromwell had paused to survey the countryside, say that this was a land worth fighting for. That's what Bro. Ultan had told us in history lessons, loading the words with such significance that my heart nearly burst with pride to think that Cromwell had thought so highly of this place. Our place.

And there was Kilnockin Hill smaller than the others, always wearing a yellow blaze of furze in springtime. On high ground overlooking the town was the railway station and beyond were Knockinglass and Mockler's Hill, veiled in a thin, smoky-blue haze.

Those hills were the recognizable boundaries of our world. Beyond them lay another, unknown world of winding roads that stretched away from us, past cottages and farmhouses, through town lands and on to distant, mysterious places inhabited by strange people: there was Cashel and its Rock, there was the small station at Farnaleen, where trains stopped on their way to and from Dublin. And further away, Thurles, where the beet trains went in October. Most of the people who left the town by train were emigrants travelling in the opposite direction: through Clonmel, Carrick and on to Rosslare to get the boat to England. All those places were merely names to us, shrouded in mystery.

And behind us, rising above all, was the soft blue bulk of Sliabhhamon. Our mother-mountain: everpresent, unchanging, a reassuring guardian watching over all. Countless eyes had found comfort there through the centuries. Many people that we had known were seeing it now in faraway places through the eye of memory.

Below us a man rattled around a meadow on a horse-drawn hay-rake gathering grasscocks of hay into heaps for men to fork into haycocks. Somewhere a corncrake sounded its screeching call.

A word from Horse and we were off again. Onto the Boody Bridge that spanned the railway line where it cut across an old Mass path, down the wooden stairs then along the sleepers until we arrived at the gate that led into a field bounding the wood. A metal sign fixed to the gate warning of penalties if it should be left open. Here we stopped and gazed across to the hunting gate where we would enter the wood.

Horse dropped to his knees, pressed an ear to the gleaming track that curved away through the wood. Paudie knelt and put his ear to the other track. Just the way we'd seen the Indians do it in films.

'There's one coming,' Horse said, 'about an hour's time.'

Horse was the only one who could hear a train coming.

'That's the half-three train,' said Judo, 'sure we all know that'll be on in an hour.'

Horse grabbed Judo by the throat.

'Are you making out I can't hear the train?'

'No, no Horse, I'm not, I'm sorry Horse, I was only saying...'

'Well, don't be only saying any feckin thing or I'll throttle ya.'

Everyone knew you couldn't hear a train like that, unless maybe you had ears like an Indian. But nobody was going to go against Horse.

A few minutes later we were climbing the hunting gate,

tumbling over it and into the wood.

We ran along an uphill path: briars scratching bare legs, tall frondy ferns leaning out to brush our faces. Slithering sometimes on muddy patches that were slow to dry in the shade of the trees away from the heat of the sun. About fifty yards into the wood Horse stopped.

And suddenly he was lowering his voice, beginning to skulk, as though fearing detection. Instinctively we began to move in the same way. What we all feared most was being chased by the gamekeeper. And worse than being chased: being caught.

Following Horse's orders we left the path and fanned out searching for hazel trees.

It didn't take long and soon Paudie was chopping at thick offshoots with the kindling hatchet.

Horse sent Judo and me further along the path to act as lookouts.

'Remember now, give us a boodle if that shaggin gamekeeper appears,' Horse said.

We wandered aimlessly away from the others, aware of the distance growing between them and us, feeling a little exposed, but not worried by it.

Finally we crept into the cool, gloomy shade of a clump of laurels that overlooked the path. Not paying much attention to our duties as lookouts. Judo was showing me his collection of chewing-gum cards. The ones that you got whenever you bought three-penny packets of the new chewing gum that came in the shape of golf balls. Everybody was collecting the pictures that came with them. Mostly they were pictures of pop stars, like the Swinging Blue Jeans, Billy J. Kramer, the Beatles and others.

'This group is called The Cascades,' Judo was saying.

I wasn't really interested in Judo's cards.

Or The Cascades.

'Little shy girl if only you were my girl...' he sang.

'What d'ya think of Esther Hartigan?' he asked suddenly.

I thought for a minute.

'You mean *Skinny* Hartigan?'

'Yeah, yeah, Skinny.'

'Why would I be thinking about Skinny Hartigan?'

'I dunno... I kinda like her.'

'Jaysus Judo, she's a feckin a girl, when did you start liking girls, you'll be kissing 'em like aul' Georgy Porgy next.'

Just then I heard a sound.

'Listen.'

Someone was moving along the path. Moving in our direction. I could hear the crackle of breaking twigs, the swish of ferns on trouser legs.

'Jaysus is that him?' Judo asked.

'I can't see through the ferns.'

'You better boodle, it has to be him.'

Judo was edging to run.

I waited.

Until I saw the tweedy hat with fishing-flies hooked on its band. I didn't need to see more.

We ran, forgetting to give the warning boodle.

A shout came from behind.

'Hey, ye little hoors.'

That shout sent a rush of terror through me. Minutes later we were tearing into the middle of the gang, shouting, warning, and then we were all running towards the hunting gate. Me bringing up the rear. Terrified I'd fall and be caught, expecting at any moment that he would gain on me and grab me by the neck.

We didn't stop running until we'd burst from the wood and reached the Boody Bridge. Gasping and panting. Cursing. Talking in excited bursts. Looking back towards the wood we saw him slowly push the hunting gate open, squinting as he looked all around, then stop when he realised that chasing after us would be futile.

Horse cupped his hands around his mouth and shouted.

'G'wan ya aul' cripple, ya, you'll never catch us, we're the fucken Valley gang.'

Galligan seemed to be gazing in our direction. When he began walking across the field towards the railway line we took off again, running across the Doctor's Hill.

'We'll head back for our poles in the morning, it'll take more than that aul' effer to stop us,' Horse said later, when we'd reached the safety of Jesuits' Walk.

# 6

## Work Gets In The Way

Next morning, though, there were jobs to be done. Messages to be run before we were free to gallivant. Promises to be kept: the weeding that we'd dodged the day before, that would have to be tackled.

That's how it always was, adults putting barriers between us and our pleasures. Always jobs to be done. Jobs that we either dodged, or got out of the way as quickly and painlessly as possible. Driving the mother to distraction with our moaning and whinging, our evasions, our attempts to offload our jobs onto someone else. Gerry and Frank could only do small jobs in the house like bringing out the ashes and carrying in sticks for the fire. Or rocking baby Tom to sleep or feeding him his goody without choking him.

Spuds had to be dug and vegetables brought in from the plot. Water had to be drawn from the Judy in the chipped enamel bucket with the blue rim.

If Ned Bulfin, the milkman, arrived on his pony and cart someone had to bring the sweet gallon out to have it filled with milk.

And if you were the one and Josie Barrett, or Mary Croke, or Ellie Power, were there before you you'd be sure of a long wait. They'd have to discuss the weather, their health and the dead or dying, before getting on to the saucier gossip and anything else that might come up.

If Josie Barrett got an opening at all she'd take off on a solo run.

'Howya Ned?' she'd ask.

'Not too bad Josie, good aul' day enough, ain't it?'

Mentioning the weather to Josie was always a fatal mistake.

She'd be off immediately. On and on she'd go, like a never-ending guitar riff: it would either be a bad day, good day, great day, fine day, miserable day, sunny day, wet day, bitch of a day, better day than yesterday, worse day than yesterday, and did ya ever see the like o' the rain that fell d'other day and they had ne'er a drop atall out around Coolmoyne, could ya credit that and the way it spilled here, and the like o' the hate we had last week, oh sure I'm not able for all that hate atall but Mickey Kearney said they're giving great weather from Saturday into next week, but, as I always say to Pad, as long as we don't get wind, I'm not able for that wind atall, atall, I do be in dread of that wind, sure the wind can do fierce depredation, so it can, sure a slate offa the roof could sweep the head clane offa yer shoulders, (and me standing there thinking, if only a slate would fly right now) but sure that's the way the summer slips away, ain't it?

That's the way it slips away all right, I'd be thinking, slips away while you're waiting for your milk, standing around listening to guffy aul' ones going on and on about the shaggin weather. And when the weather was dealt with it would be on to their aches and pains and the state of their health. There would be a kind of competition as they vied with one another to see who was nearest death's door: are ya well, sure I'm not too bad, I suppose – arrah, you're looking good anyway, you're not looking too bad yerself, sure aren't you as good now as you deserve to be.

Ellie Power would chime in then, speaking in quavering, doom-laden tones:

'I ask you now, what way could I be, and me with a hiatus hernia down on top o' me ulster to say nothing of me varicose veins and corns that do be burning the feet offa me anytime I put a foot under me and poor Pad with his bad hip and his water not running the way it should and sure he'd be entitled to the blind pension if that aul' welfare officer was any good at all and he not able to see the clock on the feckin mantlepiece. And ain't it wicked to the world about Johnny Hurley and the bad aul' knockout he's after getting and they says he's not going to do any good at all, at all, I believe he's after being anointed and all, so he is, I ask you now, does anyone know from one day to the next,

31

but sure Johnny always had a wake aul' chest, smoked too many Woodbines so he did.'

And then it would be time for the deaths: Mary so and so is after dying, the Lord have mercy on her, and where's this her people were from at all? And what age woman would she be now, and what time is she going to the chapel at, and where'll she be buried? Above in Calvary?

Sure that's quare, weren't all her people buried out in Red City? Of course, now that I think of it, her grandfather, he went out to Lisronagh to be buried, but sure the grandmother didn't, she said she wasn't going to go in with the Lisronagh crowd, so she went down out in Red City and Mary is going to Calvary, that must be a new plot she bought so, but sure they were always an odd aul' crowd to make the best of them...

On and on they'd go, moving effortlessly from weather, to health.

Talking, talking: about life, about death.

Almost in the one breath.

And if someone else came along a lot of what had been said would be repeated in the hope that some new slant would be revealed.

There was never any hurry because none of them was ever going anywhere.

On the morning we were to draw poles from the wood I ended up being sent to Henehan's grocery shop for sugar. And had to stand there willing Tom Brown to hurry on, please Tom, stop beaming at me and hurry on, I have to go to the wood, build a camp, break free to the enjoyable part of the day. The rest of the gang won't wait for me, and I don't want to be left behind. I hate being left behind.

But no, Tom eased himself around the shop at his own pace: sober, reflective, heedless of my impatience. Moving in slow motion behind the counter. I wondered if his big black boots that gleamed like glass were weighing him down. Slowly he lifted the lid of a storage bin, gazed deeply inside, scooped sugar into a brown bag, balanced the brass weights to the quarter-pound, then carefully folded down the top of the bag. Then looked at me over glasses balanced on the tip of his nose as he entered it in our book.

An eternity later I was running across Jesuits' Walk, anxious to catch up with the gang, left behind as usual.

When I got to Boody Bridge I met them dragging the first batch of poles along the railway line.

I fell in beside them. Not minding the abuse I received, just glad to be back with the gang again.

# 7

# Farewell

Saturday came, the final day of Kennedy's visit. We'd spent the morning dragging the last of the poles from the wood to the camp. The makings of our teepees were gathered, all we had to do now was build them. But Kennedy was the attraction for me that Saturday. He was going away and it was like the circus leaving town. There would be an end to the strange air of expectancy that had taken hold of everyone since he'd arrived.

From that Saturday on, though, it would be back to the ordinary again.

I'd arrived at Mamie Mackey's half-door, all set to watch his departure on her telly. I'd left our kitchen because the mother was listening to him on the radio with the volume turned up high.

Mamie had painted her front door red only the week before. It stood out like a bright beacon beside the greys, browns and greens of the neighbouring doors.

'Sure I have to have it lookin' right in case Kennedy calls for the tay,' she'd said, blotches of red paint on her hands, red smears on the door lintels.

Hers was the only house on the road with a telly. A magnet it was to us in the evening when we'd come back from our gallivanting. Sidling up to it, drawn by the shifting light from the bright screen in the far corner of that gloomy kitchen. The lure of other worlds beaming from that box. There we'd stand, oblivious to the dewy air settling on us as darkness gathered at our backs. Engrossed in one of the eight million stories from *The Naked City*. Or watching *The Twilight Zone*.

'Ye'll go blind from watching that feckin yoke, they says 'tis terrible bad for the eyes,' Mary Croke would say to us.

But it would have taken a lot more than Mary Croke's nagging to break the hold that the telly had taken on us.

Or stop us coming back early from our gallivanting on Thursdays to watch the *Everglades* and Lincoln Vail zooming around in his airboat keeping law and order. Mamie was always there sitting on that old Morris Minor car seat that served as a sofa. Cigarette smoke swirling around her black hair. Curling towards the bare rafters of the roof above. If the programme we wanted to watch had already started she'd tell us what was happening. Unless Johnny, her peevish brother with the razor-edged tongue, was there, then she'd pretend not to notice us at all, hoping he wouldn't either. But he'd see us eventually and squeal in his high-pitched voice:

'Get away from the door ye little scuts.'

'You're worse to let them gawk in over the door like that, why don't you hunt them, why do you always leave it to me?' he'd say to Mamie, driving us away with a wave of the sweeping brush.

But quietly, shiftily, we'd re-appear at the doorway again, hoping he wouldn't notice. Usually he did.

'Can't you let the childer watch the flaming thing, it'll be over in a few minutes,' Mamie would say, getting vexed.

'Go on, scoot, I'm not running a feckin cinema here, that's across the road and ye have to pay to get in there, so ye have, anyway it's time to be closing the door, before the moths start coming in.'

If he closed the door we'd run off and sneak into the Bridge Bar. But we'd be hunted from there too. That left only While-U-Wait's window where there were tellies on display. There we'd have pictures but no sound.

Sometimes Johnny would stay in the bedroom with their mother who was bedridden. Then there wouldn't be any interruptions.

'He's inside edging that tongue of his,' Mamie would say, with a jerk of her head towards the bedroom door.

At this time of day though, he was at work in the laundry run by the nuns.

'You're just in time, Jonno,' Mamie said, as I placed my elbows on the half-door.

35

'How did ya know 'twas me?' I asked.

'Aha, now, aul' Mamie have eyes in the back of her poll,' she said.

Kennedy was sitting, listening, looking really interested, while some aul' one with a big hat talked on and on.

'Will that one with the hat ever shut up,' Mamie said, flicking a butt into the fire.

At last Kennedy got up and gave a long speech. Nearly the last thing he said was that he would like to come back sometime to see old Shannon's face once more.

'He's a handsome divil all right,' Mamie sighed.

It was sad somehow, strangely sad, watching Kennedy walk up those steps, turn, wave, smile, disappear into that plane. Even sadder to watch it taxi off to the runway, then rise slowly, miraculously, into a gunmetal grey sky to be swallowed up in great banks and ridges of cloud. I hadn't felt that sad since the end of *Old Yeller*, sitting there in the cinema, eyes fixed on the screen, the words of that song echoing out: 'Old Yeller, come back Yeller,' lost in the emotion of another world, knowing that Old Yeller was dead. Shot. Gone. Forever.

'Ah, 'tis a pity, alannah,' Mamie said, 'he's gone, sure what are we going to do now?'

# 8

# End Of June

Sunday afternoon, racing along The Valley, just out of the cinema.
Kennedy's departure forgotten. Josie Barratt with her huge
breasts resting on the rim of the half-door. *Whoosh* – I buried an
arrow in the cleavage. And *whoosh* I left another quivering in Mary
Croke's bony forehead at the next half-door.

'Will ye slow down, will ye,' Mamie Mackey called.

She was leaning over her half-door, one arm raised, hand
parallel to her cheek, Woodbine between fingers as usual.
Wearing one of those cross-over aprons. Her face framed by a
thick mop of curly black hair. Glasses sitting slightly askew on her
nose. When she coughed it seemed as though something was
ripping and tearing in her chest.

'Where are ye off to in such a hurry?' she asked.

I stopped, Judo as well. Paudie, Jim, Horse and the rest of the
gang ran on.

'We're heading for the Abbey Rocks, Mamie,' Judo said.

'To play cowboys and Indians, is it?'

'Yeah, we're gonta be Apaches, 'cos we just seen *Apache
Territory*,' I said.

'Oh, that Rory Calhoun is a handsome divil,' Mamie sighed.

'Which of ye is going to be Big Chief Sitting Bull?' she asked
then, flicking her Woodbine butt into the road.

'Sitting Bull wasn't an Apache, he was chief of the Sioux,' I
said.

'Oh, excuse *me*, I thought they were all just feckin redskins,'
she said.

'Geronimo and Cochise, they were Apache chiefs,' Judo said.

'Was Rory Calhoun Geronimo in the film?' Mamie asked.

'For feck's sake, Mamie, Rory Calhoun was a cowboy,' Judo
said.

'Never,' said Mamie.

'Horse, I suppose, or our Paudie'll be the chiefs, they always get the principal parts,' I said.

'Yeah, Horse'll be dead on as Crazy Horse, he's Horse and he's shaggin well crazy as well,' said Judo.

'Are ye finished building yeer camp?' Mamie asked.

'Nearly,' I said.

'I suppose we'll never see ye now, ye'll be in that feckin camp morning, noon and night, when yeer not off gallivantin'?' she said.

'It's a real Indian camp, not just cardboard boxes and bushes like before,' Judo said.

'G'way outa that,' she said, 'faith now, and I'll have to come and have a look when yeer finished and settled in, like.'

'Ya can't,' Judo said, 'you're too old. And anyway it's in a secret place.'

'A secret place, faith,' she answered.

'And no girls can come to our camp – or be in our gang either,' I said.

'Well whisht, amn't I lucky to be let live at all. But sure now, 'tis a long time since I was a girl,' Mamie said.

'Hey, c'mere 'till I be telling ye,' she said then.

We looked at her.

'D'ye know what? There's a great picture coming to the Capitol in a fortnight's time, 'tis gonta run for a full week.'

Mamie always read *The Nationalist* on Thursdays and knew what films were on the way.

'A *week*,' I said.

I remembered a film had once run in the Capitol for three whole days. A holy picture, about a boy, his sick donkey and Francis of Asissi's tomb. We'd even gotten a half-day from school to see a special matinee showing. On account of it being a holy picture. Philly Landy had cried when the sick donkey died.

'Yep, a full week,' said Mamie.

'Jay, it must be some flick,' Judo said.

'It'll be in Cinemascope.'

'What's that?'

'They're going to have to make the screen wider, so they can fit all the horses and Mexicans in,' Mamie said.

Make the screen bigger, horses and Mexicans, I thought.

*Jaysus.*

We waited in suspense as she looked from one to the other of us. Still she waited, wanting to keep us hanging.

'It's a cowboy film,' she said, then paused again.

'Ah, c'mon Mamie,' Judo said.

'It's called *The Magnificent Seven.*'

Yul Brynner, Steve McQueen, she said, they were going to be the principal actors.

'Oh, they're handsome divils, them two,' said Mamie.

Handsome meant nothing to me.

She told us what it would be about and we knew straight away that it was the kind of film that we loved. A small band battling against overwhelming odds. Peasants against ruthless Mexican banditos wearing big moustaches and sombreros.

'Deadly,' Judo said.

'We have to go Mamie,' I said.

Off we ran.

Dying to tell the others.

# 9

# Into July

We were at the kitchen table, all six of us, kneeling on the forms, sprinkling sugar onto our cornflakes. Milk puddles forming on the oil-cloth covering the table, seeping into knife-slits.

'Go aisy on that sugar, let ye, or 'twill rot the teeth out o' yeer heads,' the mother was saying.

She was feeding goody to baby Tom who shook the pram violently whenever there was too long a pause between spoonfuls.

Until that summer we'd never tasted cornflakes. Had never crunched them, milky and sugary, in our mouths. Kennedy, cornflakes, the new Merseybeat music, Judo's transistor: the world was throwing new things our way all the time.

'Don't forget one of ye has to dig out a message bag of spuds for the dinner before ye take off gallivantin,' I think 'tis your turn Jonno.'

The mother was fixing two huge safety pins in Tom's nappy.

'No it's not, Mam,' I said.

'Yes it is so,' Paudie said, 'I did it yesterday.'

'Yeah, but it's your turn to empty the smelly, stinking bucket,' I jeered.

Emptying the bucket was the worst job of all.

'But Mam, I want to go with the lads, we're finishing our teepees today, can't I dig the spuds later on,' I said.

'Dig them now, God knows what time ye'll be back at, 'twill only take a few minutes,' she answered.

They ran off then, Paudie and Jim, ushering Gerry, Frank and Joe out the door ahead of them.

I sauntered out to the plots, feeling sorry for myself, imagining what was going on at the camp while I was stuck in the plots digging spuds for the dinner. Missing out. Pad Shea, a pipe-smoking old veteran of the Great War to my left, to my right

Dinnsy O'Brien, who never had a job because of some mysterious 'wakeness' that afflicted him. The father said the 'wakeness' only came over him when work was mentioned.

I dug awkwardly, frantically, growing more and more frustrated as potatoes were impaled on the crooked prongs of the fork.

'Take your hour, young fella, take your hour,' Pad said, puffing contentedly.

An hour later I was running along the railway line, heart thumping, anxious to get to the camp, hoping I hadn't missed anything.

When I crawled from the briary tunnel into the brightness of the clearing where we were building our camp the skeletons of two teepees had been raised. Horse was standing on a barrel, swearing, using binding twine to secure four poles that had been laid one against another in a cone-shape above his head. More poles were added and tied until there was just enough space left to remove the barrel and create a flap for entering the teepee. Paudie and Horse then began weaving thin switches through the poles to strengthen the structure.

Before starting on the final teepee Horse and Paudie summoned Judo and me.

'The two of ye are to go to Dansie's and see if he has any aul' sacks that he doesn't want,' Horse said.

'We're going to use them to cover the poles,' Paudie said.

'Well, we can't shaggin well get buffalo skins can we?' he said, seeing the look on our faces.

Dansie, the fuel merchant, would probably expect us to do some work in return for any sacks he might give us.

'But I want to stay here at the camp, I don't want to go cadging dirty sacks offa Dansie,' I said.

'Yeah, me too,' Judo said.

'D'ye want to be thrown outa the gang, do ye? Feck off down to Dansie's now and get some sacks,' Horse said, making a threatening move towards us.

We headed away from the camp along the railway line,

41

intending to cut through the cattle pens at the railway station and onto the Cashel road, using a circuitous route, hoping to fool the Patrick's Place gang. We knew they'd be trying to find the location of our camp. In order to wreck it.

'Hey, look,' Judo said.

Coming towards us along the railway line was a dog trailing a lead. It was Fritz, Brother Virgilius' sausage dog. His pride and joy. Fat, well-groomed, his coat shining like one of Larry Keating's racehorses. Virgilius had a special whistle for controlling him. Its sound was beyond the range of human hearing. He'd demonstrated it to us one day in the school hurling field. One silent blast and Fritz had come running.

'Where da feck did he come from?' Judo asked.

'He must have gotten away when Virgy was taking his morning stroll,' I said.

Almost every day Brother Virgilius could be seen strolling along the Cashel road that ran below and parallel to the railway line. Fritz trotting obediently beside him on the end of a leather lead.

He was licking Judo's hand, gratefully it seemed.

'I bet he doesn't want to go back to aul' frostballs Virgy,' I said.

'Made his escape like a P.O.W.' said Judo.

'A bold bid for freedom,' I said.

I'd read that in a sixty-four page Commando comic.

'Will we keep him?' Judo asked.

'Keep him? Jaysus, Judo, I dunno,' I said.

'We could have him as a mascot,' Judo said.

'Indian warriors don't have mascots, and if Virgy found out he'd have the sergeant onto us,' I said.

'And kill us when we go back in September,' said Judo.

Keeping him would not be good for our health.

We pondered for a while, wondering what we should do. Other than bring him straight up to Virgilius at the monastery.

'We'll hold on to him for a while, tie him up in the bushes, maybe aul' Virgy will give a reward to whoever finds him, then we can bring him up to the monastery and claim it,' said Judo.

I had my doubts about that plan, especially the notion that Virgilius would give a reward, particularly if Judo and I were the finders.

We led him into the bushes beside the railway line, tied him to a whitethorn, then headed off to Dansie's to cadge sacks.

'So long Fritz,' says Judo.

And then of course, when we got to the Cashel road who should we meet but Virgy, walking along, whistle on a string around his neck. He looked strange, in his black suit and hat without the soutane and green sash. The vicious glint was still in his eye, though.

'Jaysus Judo,' I muttered.

'Don't panic,' Judo said.

'Where have you boys been?' Virgy asked, without so much as an hello.

'On the railway line, bruh,' says Judo.

'Have you seen any sign of Fritz?'

'Not a sign, didn't see hide nor hair of him, bruh,' Judo answered.

'What happened bruh, did he get away on ya?' I asked.

'Are you stupid, boy, isn't it obvious that he got away from me? If you must know, we were taking our morning stroll when we met some idiot with four greyhounds on leashes. They lunged at Fritz and while I was waving my brolly he got away and ran off into the fields.'

'Oh, that'd be Timmy Fitzpatrick, bruh, sure me father said his aul' dogs wouldn't run outa yer way,' Judo said.

Virgy nearly melted him with a look.

'Won't he come to the whistle, bruh,' I asked, quickly.

'He's probably out of earshot now and too traumatised to respond.'

'What's traumatised, bruh?' I asked, deferentially.

'It's a kind of shock, you get it when something bad happens to you,' he snapped.

I had a terrible feeling that Judo and I were putting ourselves in line for some traumatising.

'We'll keep an eye out for him bruh, will ya be giving out a reward, bruh?' Judo asked.

'Don't be cheeky boy,' he snapped.

'I'll be telling the sergeant that he's missing,' he said, walking away, blowing his silent whistle.

'The feckin sergeant, did ya hear him, he's telling the feckin sergeant, we'll be in right trouble now,' I said.

'Say nothing to no-one about this,' says Judo. 'This could be worth half a crown to us.'

Two hours later we were finally back in the camp, hands, clothes and faces blackened from carrying old coal bags given to us by Dansie. It had taken several trips to get them all to the camp-site. They were no good for fuel anymore because the bottoms had rotted away. Dansie had tested every one with a jerk of his big hands before parting with it. And made us weigh and fill several bags of coal from the scoop of his big scales.

'Ye'll get nothing for nothing in this life, me boyos,' Dansie had said.

The sacks were perfect for us and soon the bare poles were clad in brown hemp sacking, threadbare in places, with 'Sutton Coals 1/2 a cwt' written on them in red lettering.

Our Indian camp was almost complete, almost real.

Evening had come and we were hungry. We ran off home to the supper.

After supper Judo and I sneaked back to check on Fritz and bring him something to eat. I had a few jammy crusts in my pocket. Left-overs from the supper. Usually thrown into an old message bag for Mrs. Morrissey's hens. I'd saved a few for Fritz. When I offered them to him he sniffed, turned his nose up.

'The little fecker,' said Judo.

'He's probably used to having the best o' mate everyday,' I said.

'That stringy little shagger probably gets more mate in a day than the two of us would get in a week.'

'Probably.'

'Well used to it like his well-fed master.'

'What class of a head have he on him at all,' said Judo, 'that fecker'd nearly talk to ya.'

'Probably ask ya the twelve times tables,' I said.

I'd often suffered at Virgy's hands on account of the twelve times tables.

'Willya look at the little shagger, he's kind of accusing us of something,' Judo said.

We went off planning to come back next morning and take him to the monastery, hoping to be paid some kind of reward.

# 10

# Bringing Fritz Home

Next morning we were hurrying back along the line again. Judo was nonchalant, boastful almost, but I was anxious to be rid of Fritz.

'He'll surely give us half a dollar,' Judo was saying, then speculating on what he'd do with his half.

'I should really be entitled to more than half, you know, seeing 'twas my idea,' he said, looking at me.

I was looking ahead along the gleaming tracks trying to capture the heat shimmer that wiggled and danced above them, thinking they looked like thin black threads. We were getting close to the place where we'd hidden Fritz when my eyes came to rest on something lying between the tracks. Something dark. With a lead attached.

'Oh, Jaysus, Judo, willya look willya.'

We stopped. Ran forward. It was Fritz. Or what was left of him. He had been severed in two neat halves. He must have been caught by a train as he straddled the line.

'Oh, Jaysus, Fritz, what are ya after doing on us?' I said.

Poor Fritz was lying there his little head pointed accusingly towards us.

'Juh know why that happened, Jonno,' Judo said, all knowledgeable, 'cos he was a sausage dog, he was just too shaggin long, like, his arse was too far behind him, he couldn't get it across the feckin line fast enough.'

'He's rightly shagged now, Judo, and so are we,' I said, a terrible dread rising in me.

Judo had taken Fritz's severed rear end by the tail.

'You take the other half there Jonno and we'll lug him back to his master,' he said.

'Jaysus, he'll kill us, Judo, 'twas our fault, I knew we

46

should've brought him back yesterday, I knew it, I feckin well knew it, we're in right trouble now, 'tis we'll be traumatised, I can tell ya, when Virgy is finished with us,' I roared.

'Lookit Jonno, we'll tell him we were strolling along the railway line, minding our own business like, heading for our camp, when next thing we nearly tripped over the two halves of poor Fritz, he's not going to know any different,' Judo said.

'I dunno, Judo, I dunno, maybe we should just leave him for someone else to find,' I said.

'We will in our arse, and let them get the reward? C'mon don't be so windy, grab him by the collar there.'

I grabbed the collar and lifted. Horrible stringy things dangled from Fritz.

'No wonder he wouldn't ate the crusts for us, sure there's a good pound of sausages hanging outa the little fecker,' Judo said.

'Maybe we should get a bag,' I said.

'Naw, c'mon, we'll be there in no time.'

It was a long walk to the monastery, pieces of Fritz streeling on the ground as we went. Leaving red smudges.

'God bless the mark, what are ye after doing, is it a Christian ye have or what?' Rachel Horan said, blessing herself as we passed.

My heart pounded as we walked up the path to the side-door of the monastery. Mary Hally, the housekeeper, answered to our ring.

'Glory be to God,' she said, staggering a little when she saw what we were carrying.

She pointed towards the garden.

Virgilius was working at an onion bed, his coat off, exposing horrible white arms with wormy red hair.

'In the name o' God,' he said, when he saw the piece of Fritz that I was carrying.

And the remainder of him that Judo had by the tail.

'We found the two halves of him on the railway line bruh, the poor divil, sure he must have run under the nine-thirty last night,' Judo said, in what he thought was a sympathetic tone.

47

I braced myself.

For a long moment Virgy stared in silence. In class his silences usually ended in violent eruptions. I waited, preparing for immediate flight. No eruption came. Virgy seemed to have lost his speech for a moment.

'We thought we'd better bring the bits up to you bruh, didn't we Jonno?' Judo nodded at me.

Encouraging me to say something.

I said nothing.

Because I was thinking, oh please shut up, Judo, keep your gob shut, Judo, while we're still in one piece.

Judo's voice seemed to break the trance that had gripped Virgy.

'How do you know what train he went under?' he asked, fixing a suspicious eye on Judo.

On me.

'Well, he wasn't on the line yesterday evening bruh, we looked after we met you bruh, and we found him this morning, on our way to our camp bruh, cut clane in two so he was, but sure, he probably didn't even know what hit him, sure he wouldn't have been expecting a train to come on in the dark like, would he?' Judo said.

'Shut up, you idiot,' Virgilius said.

He had turned pale, was standing sideways to us, keeping Fritz's remains out of his sight. I felt our chances of a reward were well gone. He ordered me to the tool shed for two spades, brought us to a corner of the garden, told us to bury Fritz. He went back to his onion bed.

'Some reward, all right,' I said, 'digging a shaggin grave for Fritz.'

We paused occasionally from our digging, took stock of the school, eerie and quiet, its blank dark windows like evil eyes looking at us. I didn't like being so close to it during our holidays.

'He'll give us something, wait'll ya see, he'll give us a tanner apiece, well, maybe a thruppeny bit,' Judo said, scaling down his expectations.

It took us the best part of an hour to get Fritz under the clay. Before putting him in his hole Judo removed the collar and lead.

'I better ask him if he'd like to say a prayer over Fritz before we plant him,' Judo said, strolling over to Virgy.

'JUST BURY HIM,' Virgy roared.

After that he put us weeding his lettuce and beetroot beds.

He worked away at his onions throwing occasional, murderous glances in our direction. I could see he was pondering our story, Judo's story, suspected us of something but wasn't quite sure what.

'There's gonta be no escape, and no friggin reward, we should have left that shaggin mutt on the railway line, look at us now, how are we gonta get away from here?' I said to Judo.

'Twill be dinnertime soon, he'll have to go in for his grub, you know how fond the monks are of their big feeds, an he'll have his little nap after it. But as soon as ever he goes inside that door we'll hook it,' Judo said.

'What'll we do if he tells the sergeant, if they bring us to the barracks for a third degree?' I asked.

That's what happened in gangster films.

'Naw, he won't get the sergeant,' Judo answered.

Finally a bell went somewhere in the monastery and Virgy beckoned to us.

'This is it,' says Judo, elbowing me, seeing Virgy put his hand in his pocket.

But all he pulled out was a white handkerchief.

'I'm looking forward to seeing you boys in September, you'll both be spending another year in sixth class, won't you – I take it your mothers will hardly waste money sending a pair of scholars like you to the secondary?' he said.

To me it sounded more a threat than a question.

'That's right bruh,' I said.

'Good,' he said, staring hard at us, 'Good.'

That sounded ominous, as if he was making a promise to himself.

We lingered on the doorstep as he pulled on his slippers,

hoping. But nothing came.

'Hungry aul' shagger, and not even a thank you for bringing Fritz home and giving him a dacent burial, we shoulda left him on the line and let the crows have a right feed on him, the little effer,' Judo said, swinging the lead in a loop, the collar slapping off the ground.

'He'll definitely have it in for us in September,' I said.

'Maybe we can flog the collar and lead to some aul' one,' Judo said.

I kept seeing that hard-eyed look Virgilius had given us.

But, sure, September is an eternity away, I told myself.

# 11

# An Ambush

Our teepees were built. The camp was finished. It would be our base, our haven from the adult world, our secret hideaway for the rest of the summer.

Most mornings we'd have a powwow at the camp, then off we'd go, gallivanting in search of adventure and distraction. This morning we had our war paint on, were on the banks of the Clashawley. On an open space, adjacent to The Valley on one side, the river on the other. A stretch of the old town wall ran parallel to the river along its far bank. Forming a barrier between us, the ancient yews of the Protestant churchyard and the jagged tower-top high above.

The morning was overcast, close, the air thick and heavy with the sound of bees, flies, grasshoppers, birds, dogs. A horse neighing somewhere. A distant tractor. All blending into a monotonous, deadening drone. The drone of summer. The tedium of happy days. Occasionally a horse and cart clattered by on its way to the creamery further down The Valley. In the field behind Horse's house men were slowly piking hay onto a horse-drawn trolley that rolled along on wide, iron wheels. Slanted poles at front and rear held the hay in place. I could hear the voices of the men as they paused now and again to smoke and exchange desultory banter.

It was the first week of July. We were idling around, irritable from the heaviness of it all. Not really doing anything. The river had run low. Judo and I were prowling through the rushes close to the bank, arrow in bow, hoping to come across a water hen.

The smell of drying river-moss strong in my nostrils.

Chasing water hens was a waste of time. A rustle in the rushes, a brief flash of dark feathers and the hen was gone. That's all you'd see of water hens. Not even a chance to get off an arrow.

Still we prowled, pointlessly.

'This is feckin useless,' Judo said, finally.

Boredom was setting in. We needed a diversion.

I looked to the riverbank.

Just then Foxy Burke came rattling down The Valley on his father's jennet and cart hauling his one churn of milk to the creamery. The jennet was big and mostly black. He strode along, all raised head, twitching ears and swishing tail. Eyes wild inside the winkers. Wire bit pulled tight in his mouth. He was hard to stop even when only walking. There was always a feeling that he could take off at any moment; that Foxy, no-one, would be able to stop him at full tilt.

The big jennet strode purposefully on. Foxy barely managed to wave and call to us.

'The fecker is pulling like a train lads,' he shouted.

When they were out of sight Horse called us together.

'I have a deadly idea,' he said.

'What is it?' Paudie asked.

'We'll pretend that Foxy is driving a stage coach and we'll ambush him on the way back,' Horse said.

The prospect of the ambush–hiding, waiting, charging after Foxy's big jennet– lifted the lethargy that had been bearing down on us.

A low wall ran parallel to the road as far as Stokes' old mill. From the spot where wall and mill met we would launch the ambush, Horse and Paudie decided.

As usual, Judo and I were sent as scouts to see how long it would take Foxy to get out of the creamery.

In the creamery yard there was a long queue of farmers waiting to offload their milk. Horse, pony, and ass-drawn carts; Prefects, Anglias, Cambridges with trailers behind; old Ferguson and Fordson Major tractors – all were stretched in a stalled line across the yard and out onto the road. Foxy was about halfway in the queue. We chatted with him.

'It's gonta take me another half an hour to get out of this feckin place,' he moaned, gazing at two farmers with folded arms propped by their arses against the wing of an Anglia.

'Then I have to bring separated milk back for the calves, and a butt of crushed oats, and give the rest of the feckin day turning hay with the aul' fella in the Back field,' Foxy said.

'And 'tisn't great hay weather either,' he said, sorrowfully, 'not great drying there at all.' Probably echoing his aul' fella, who always wore a long, sorrowful face even when there was good hay weather.

The jennet was restless, shaking his obstinate head, stamping, kicking at flies beneath his belly, twitching muscles when they landed on his body.

'Can I drive the jennet up The Valley?' Judo asked.

'Oh Jaysus no Judo, no-one can drive that jennet only me and the aul' fella, he takes an awful howlt, only for we do have an extra big winkers on him he'd be gone in a minute, all 'twould take is an aul' flying sweet paper,' Foxy said.

The jennet shook his entire body, as if in agreement with Foxy, giving himself a fright when the draught chains rattled against the shafts.

'Aisy, aisy, stand aisy ya shaggin cripple,' Foxy said, jerking hard on the reins.

We went back onto the road and into Ned Meagher's shop to buy a pennyworth of broken biscuits. Ned was cutting ham into transparent slices on his smooth-running Avery ham slicer.

'Anything else now, Mrs. Barton?' he asked, wrapping the ham, forcing a wide, false-toothed smile.

He carried her purchases out to her Austin Mini Estate with its wood inserts, thanking her profusely and fussing over her all the time.

'Broken biscuits,' he said, wearily, when we ordered.

We ate our broken Marietta biscuits from a bag before returning to the gang. Then we waited. Eventually Foxy and the jennet appeared. The cart running smoothly along on its two inflated car wheels. The only sound I could hear was the clink of the draught chains and the rapid click of the jennet's lightly shod hooves.

Judo couldn't resist pinching Pony's arse which was directly in front of him.

'Ah, ouch, ouch,' Pony shouted.

'Jaysus, will ye stay quiet,' Horse hissed.

'Go aisy, willya, go aisy,' we heard Foxy say to the jennet.

When they drew level with us we leaped from behind the wall screeching our version of the Apache war-cry. The sudden noise shocked Mom Mom Gunn's terrier from his torpor on the roadside. He charged at the jennet, barked, began snapping at his heels. Foxy roared at the dog, swiped at him with his switch. The arrows that we fired clunked off the churn and the wheels of the cart. Horse, though, had aimed one directly at the jennet's hindquarters. He hit the target. That sudden dart of pain, the dog's snapping, our screeching and Foxy's shouting, was too much for the jennet. He took off. Foxy leaned back throwing all his weight on the reins. No use. On the jennet ran, ears flattened, head outstretched, veering from side to side on the road. Skimming past the loaded hay trolley just emerging from the hayfield. Two men on top of the load looked in astonishment at the fleeing jennet.

We followed Foxy, screeching, laughing, delighted with the outcome of our ambush. Excitement sending a surge of energy through us.

On the hill close to our house a pole carrying a streetlight stood about two feet out from the wall. Approaching this pole the jennet veered wildly once more. One wheel hooked on the pole bringing jennet and cart to an abrupt halt, catapulting Foxy and the churn onto the grassy bank on the roadside. The lid flew off the churn. A flat white lake of separated milk spread across the road.

'Oh Jaysus, Jaysus help me, I'll be kilt, the aul' fella'll kill me, what am I gonta do, they'll be ne'er a sup of milk left for the calves,' Foxy roared.

The jennet had come to a standstill, appeared to have been shocked into docility. Horse and Paudie straightened the churn.

'There's still a sup in the arse o' the churn Foxy,' Paudie said.

'Oh there's only a dreeder left, I'll be kilt, I'll be kilt, an' look at me poor knees, they're all tore asunder,' Foxy lamented.

He turned his attention to the jennet and the cart. Miraculously no damage had been done to the cart.

'What class of an aul' mad cripple are you at all,' he roared at the jennet, 'you're only fit for the feckin kennels, the hounds probably wouldn't even ate ya. Or maybe the aul' fella'll sell ya to the tinkers, you'll know all about it then, so ya will, ya big black useless hoor ya.'

A row of heads had appeared over half-doors.

'Lucky the chap wadn't kilt,' Josie Barratt said, from her half-door.

'He'll be all right, 'tis nothing,' Horse said.

Between us we managed to get the churn back onto the cart.

'Let ya pull it over to the Judy Foxy and we'll top the churn back up with water, sure the calves won't know the difference if they have watery milk for one day,' Judo said.

'The aul' fella will,' Foxy said.

'Sure, Jaysus, yer aul' fella's not gonta be drinking separated milk, is he?' Horse said.

'I dunno, I dunno,' said Foxy.

Eventually he was pacified enough to get back on the cart and head for home.

'I'd say that aul' jennet is shell shocked, sure there's not a kook outa him now,' Mamie Mackey said as we walked back.

When the incident of Foxy's jennet was safely in the past it became one of the highlights of the summer. On those evenings when we lit a fire at the camp and sat around it as darkness gathered and our shadows danced on the teepees the story of Foxy's jennet would be told and retold, twisted and tweaked until the facts of what had actually happened were lost in the little legend we were creating. Still, behind the bravado of the boasting and the storytelling there was an unspoken dread that the sergeant would be calling to our door with his silver buttons and his notebook.

# 12

# The Sergeant

We were afraid of the sergeant. *Everyone* was afraid of the sergeant. The man on patrol in our town. He didn't rush to the scene of the latest crime in an airboat, like Lincoln Vail. Because there wasn't any crime. So he had plenty of time to cycle around, keep his eye on us. And if he wasn't patrolling the town one or the other of his two minions was.

We'd see him on patrol odd days, cycling omnipotently along on his big black bike, wearing bicycle clips above shining boots, a permanent scowl on his face. A dark cloud on a sunny day. Silver buttons straining and gleaming in a line over his bulging gut. He had power over us, even if we weren't doing anything wrong. He could have you sent to the reformatory at Ferryhouse where troublesome boys were taken to be straightened out.

That's what I believed.

I'd never seen the place, yet felt I knew it so often had it been threatened on us as a place of punishment if we didn't behave. Ferryhouse. Reformatory. The words tolled like an evil bell in my consciousness, arousing terrifying thoughts of hunger, cold dormitories, big straps, crew cuts. And separation.

A place where the damned were cast into outer darkness.

When Judo and I had made our trip to Clonmel by bus as a treat on the Monday following our Confirmation we'd met two palefaced boys with crew cuts in Woolworths. They'd stopped to watch us buying bon bons, and liquorice sweets, pointing to what we wanted from an array of sweets displayed in little glass display boxes. One of them said they were in Ferryhouse. At night, they told us, they slept in a huge dormitory with end-to-end beds and a brother in charge pacing up and down carrying a leather strap. They were always hungry going to bed.

As they spoke their eyes were fixed on the bon bons.

'We never get bon bons,' the oldest looking boy said.

We gave them some of ours and then they were taken roughly away by an older, cross-looking boy.

I felt vaguely glad then, glad I was free to buy my own sweets, spend my own Confirmation money – glad to be on an adventure in the big town with my friend Judo. Glad the mother was there, at home, always there, waiting for me, for all of us, to come back. Going home on the bus I was looking forward to shoving open the door to our dingy, battered kitchen, seeing the mother there, telling her all about my day in Clonmel. Because I knew she'd want to know. Would ask me lots of questions.

And I was glad too that I had only to spend school hours under the eye of the brothers: in Ferryhouse, I told the mother, they were watching over those boys even when they were in bed.

I was convinced that the sergeant could have me, any of us, sent there, to Ferryhouse, could bring me to court, have me taken away to be reformed. I wasn't sure what being 'reformed' meant. I only knew it couldn't be pleasant if it involved leather straps and dormitories.

We were determined to avoid drawing the sergeant on us. If he came patrolling along on his bike when we were at play we'd immediately stop whatever we were doing and wait until he'd passed and was well out of sight. There was always a fear in our hearts that anything we were doing would be wrong in his eyes. A feeling, always there, that we were bound to be guilty of something.

Even adults were always cautious, distrustful, and really deferential, when the sergeant or any of the guards were around.

'Ya couldn't trust them effers till they're seven years dead,' the father always said.

He was the scourge of country people coming to town at night without lights on their bikes. We'd heard many stories about the sergeant from the father and Mamie.

The father told us of a man called Smokey who'd met the sergeant one summer's night as he made his way home towards Coolmoyne after Tipperary had beaten Cork in a Munster Final.

Smokey had come into town after listening to the game on the radio. He'd spent the evening wheeling his bike from pub to pub where he discussed the finer points of the game with anyone willing to untangle his drunken observations on hurling and the weather. And the Black and Tans. Finally, he set off for home with a large bottle shoved into each of the pockets of his body coat.

He met the sergeant on the railway bridge, just above the station house on the Cashel road. He shone his torch in Smokey's face.

Recognising the sergeant and full of boozy eloquence, Smokey decided to have a bit of banter with 'that black-hearted hoor of a Kerryman.'

'Begor now sergeant, that'd be a great yoke for lamping rabbits, if a fella could get a loand of it, o'course,' Smokey said.

'Why haven't you your bike lit up?' says the sergeant.

'Sure, what lights would I want of a summer's night, don't I know me way home be now with the moon shining as bright as day? Sure I can see your aul' physog as clear as can be,' says Smokey.

He was summonsed of course. Charged with being drunk and disorderly in charge of a bicycle. And while he lived Smokey would call down an endless variety of curses on the sergeant whenever he got the chance.

We had many encounters with the sergeant. Mostly they were of no consequence, just gave rise to a tense pause in our play as we waited for him to pass by on his bike. Or tried to answer his questions correctly whenever he chose to cross-examine us about our presence in a particular place.

Always deferential, eyes on the ground, careful not to antagonise him.

Yes, sergeant. No sergeant. That's right sergeant. Oh, we will sergeant, we will.

That's how we were about a week after the adventure with Foxy when he came along as we were shooting pebbles from our catapaults, breaking bottles that we'd gathered in the dump and lined up for shooting practice. Pockets full of pebbles, filled from the pile used by the County Council workers to patch the roads. The perfect size for our catties. I was absorbed in the ritual: stretching the galabandie to its fullest extent, drawing a bead on a bottle, feeling the tension between gowlogue and galabandy, then the rubbery flap on release, the whirr of the pebble. There were cheers whenever a bottle or jamjar shattered. We'd spent a great deal of time working on our catties: finding and paring the gowlogues, cutting the galabandys from old car tyres, pulling the tongues from old shoes to make a pouch to sling the stones, getting copper wiring from an old car engine at Kennedy's garage, using it to fasten the galabandy to the gowlogues.

So absorbed were we in our game, so heated was the arguing over who had smashed what bottle, that we didn't notice the sergeant until we heard his dreaded Kerry accent.

'What d'ye think yeer doing here with them dangerous weapons, d'ye want to knock the eye outa someone's head? And all that broken glass, ye'd better be clearing that up now, if I find it there tomorrow there'll be trouble.'

We stood and watched, helpless, hating him as he grabbed each of our catties, forced the gowlogs apart and threw them in the river.

'Don't let me see ye with any more o' them yokes,' he said.

Then walked back to his bike without another word.

'Effin' aul' Black and Tan,' Horse muttered, with heartfelt bitterness.

I watched his broad black back as he swung heavily into the saddle and went creaking off on his bike. Dulling the light everywhere he went. He had made the day duller for us, and would make it duller for many more before it was over.

May you get a puncture when you're five miles away from the station, out in the middle of nowhere, I thought.

'I'd like to see *him* in the everglades,' Judo said.

'Yeah, with some big aul' alligator fastened onto his big fat arse,' I said.

'He wouldn't be worried about aul' catties then,' Judo said.

59

'Or robbing orchards.'

'Or lights on bikes.'

'Or buachalainns.'

'Or bull licences.'

'Or Smoky Walsh.'

'Or the toss school on a Sunday.'

'No, he'd be running for home with a chunk missing from his big fat arse.'

Judo ran along the riverbank, two hands clasped on his buttocks, squealing in a mock Kerry accent:

'Mammy, oh mammy, oh me arse mammy, have oo a bit of soothing cream for me poor arse mammy?'

We were screeching with laughter now, but if the sergeant re-appeared on the road we would've stopped immediately.

Reluctantly, resentfully, we set about tidying away the shards of broken glass – it wasn't going to be a threat to anyone but it was best to clean it up. Keep the sergeant happy. Keep in with him. There was no point in drawing him on us.

Images of those two boys from Ferryhouse were still fresh in my mind.

# 13

## Dan The Fisherman

Word buzzed up and down The Valley. Everyone was talking about it: Dan the fisherman was dead. And he hadn't died an ordinary death, he hadn't died in his bed like other people. Not Dan, no. He'd collapsed and died on the riverbank. Creating a big drama, giving the whole town something to talk about for days on end.

There were two fish in his basket at the time. A half-empty pack of after-dinner mints in his pocket.

A massive heart attack, people said.

'The right way to go, quick, and doing what he enjoyed,' Mamie said.

'Sure he was a grand aul' divil, never did any harm to anyone,' Ellie Power said.

The day after the ambush we walked down there, the entire gang. To see the spot where they'd found him. Fearful and fascinated. I wondered if we'd find some sign that death had been there. But there was no aura, nothing to show that a life had ended on that spot beside the river. It wasn't even creepy. There was only the water flowing along as smooth and glassy as always, rushes shifting slightly. And flattened grass on the spot where he'd died. That's all there was. We made our way home, disappointed.

Dan had been a familiar sight to all of us. Maybe too familiar.

Up or down The Valley we'd see him go, anytime of the day, any day of the week. All summer long. Well, a good part of it anyway. Strolling along with a howya Mam here, and not a bad aul' day you sir, there. Always wearing that tweedy old body coat of his, a cast off from one of the horsey crowd, and his cap with the greasy peak. Every move, every twitch of his wrinkled face, every blink, every wink of his shifting eye, saying: aren't I a trustworthy aul' fella, don't worry about me, sure I'm a harmless aul' divil altogether so I am.

Sure the childer only love it when I play games with them down there on the bank of the river.

He'd stop to chat with Pad Power, rest an elbow on his half-door, take the pipe and tobacco plug from his top pocket, pare it with his penknife, send smoke wafting sweetly on the summer air.

'How are they biting this weather, Dan?' Pad would ask, landing a spit across to the other side of the road.

'Sure they're not Pad, so they're not,' he'd answer, thumb on the bowl of his pipe. Spitting companionably into the road himself.

'I'd better be going now, sure herself'll be wondering where I am,' he'd say, when his pipe was finished.

'Sure Dan is a gas man, stone mad about the fishing, sure wouldn't he want something an' he married to an aul' split the wind like that one, and ain't he great the way he makes all them little jumps for the young lads, keeps them amused, a great man entirely.'

That's what Mary Croke had to say about Dan. And many another one said it too.

'Sure, they're innocent poor craythurs, God help them,' Dan would sometimes say, wistfully, through a swirl of pipesmoke.

A familiar character in my world was Dan, the fisherman. He didn't always walk along the road though. Often he'd appear along the riverbank. Rod in hand. Basket on his shoulder, waders shining. On his way along the river to where the best trout were. Or on his way back from fishing downriver.

'C'mere till I show ye,' he'd say, if we were playing by the riverside as he came back.

He'd lift the lid on his basket, show us his catch, a trout or two, lying silver and cold on a bed of rushes.

'What d'ye make o' them lads?' Dan would ask.

He'd lay his rod and basket on the grass. Take a penknife from his top pocket and say:

'C'mere to me now let ye and we'll have a bit o' sport.'

He'd cut slips of varying length from the clumps of snowberry bushes that grew dense and wide along the bank of the river. With a gowlogue on top.

He'd pare the sticks to a point, shove them into the ground until there were maybe eight or nine fences, some high some low.

'Now, who's gonta help me?' he'd ask.

'Me Dan, me. Can I do it Dan, can I?' the small ones would shout.

Jostling one another to get Dan's attention, be in his favour.

They'd fight and argue over who could place the sticks on the gowlogues at the top of the upright. He'd only let the small ones take part. The ones aged no more than five or six.

Sometimes, at the end of the game, he'd produce a packet of after-dinner mints as a special reward. But only for one or two lucky ones. Chosen by him. From those who submitted to his little game. Every one of them wanted that special reward.

'Yeer all to be horsies,' he'd say.

And there were more arguments over the order in which they would jump the course.

Judo and I would be aware of this going on while we waded in the river catching brickileens with jampots. Dan had no interest in us.

Those who knocked one of the cross-sticks would have to line up in front of Dan.

'How many did you knock?' he'd ask.

'Oh, bejakus now, you're not much of a horsey,' he'd say, twisting his cap back to front, making faces, sticking out his false teeth, making them laugh.

'I'll show ye a trick,' he'd say.

I'd often seen him do his trick, passing it off as something amusing, a bit of an aul' school, harmless blackguarding. And I'd laughed with him, well, maybe not laughed, more smiled uncertainly, had gone along with it – acquiesced, ignored the suspicions in the back of my mind: wondering, why, why did he want to do a thing like that?

Why put his hand there?

The little ones went along with it too: they didn't like it, but

63

he was a man, had power over them, over all of us, hadn't we all been taught to be quiet and do what adults told us? And there was always the thought of an after-dinner mint to be sucked on and savoured while others looked on jealously, craving that sweet sugary taste.

The little ones loved tricks. Except with Dan it was always the same trick.

The first time I'd seen Dan do it was with little Barney Skehan, with his white-blond hair. Standing there in his plastic sandals, without socks. He'd looked up at Dan with a one-eyed squint because of the brightness. Dan had inserted a thick finger in the waistband of his shorts, drawn it out and slid his big, calloused hand inside. He'd fondled little Barney there, letting his hand linger, before withdrawing it quickly when it seemed he was about to cry.

'Look, look, I'm after pulling out yer little taypot,' he said to Barney, showing his thumb shoved under his index finger.

Barney smiled uncertainly.

'What's he gonta do without his taypot, what'll he do at all?' he asked.

'You didn't take his taypot,' all the others shouted.

'I did.'

'No, you did not.'

'Are ye sure?'

'Yeah.'

'I'd better have a look again, so , will I have a look?'

Barney was unsure.

'Arra, 'tis only a game,' said Dan.

Again he shoved his hand inside, letting it linger a bit longer this time, fondling.

''Tis there all right, 'tis there,' he said.

And all the little faces looked up at him.

People stood around the street on the morning of his funeral shaking their heads saying wasn't it terrible sudden altogether and an awful shock to his poor wife and wasn't it a shame that Dan never had any childer of his own, and the great school he used to have with the young lads below on the bank of the river. Sure the craythurs'll miss him a fright, sure wasn't he like an uncle to them?

Wasn't he a great man now and all the sweets he used to give them, sure weren't all the little ones mad about Dan and his after-dinner mints?

# 14

# The Dump

Horse was perched on the rock that we'd set aside for the tranny. Dragging on the butt of a Boston cigarette that he'd bought loose at Lil McCarthy's. It seemed almost a sacrilege that his arse should be in contact with the rock. That rock was reserved for our sacred Sunday afternoon ritual: placing the tranny there, gathering round, listening, paying homage to the Merseybeat, to Freeman, to *Pick of the Pops*.

While we ate our Flash bars, drank our fizzy O'Brien's lemonade.

Canon Ryan wouldn't have been more offended had he gone into the church and found a knight of the road sitting on a corner of the altar having a drag. Only he could have done something about it. Unlike us.

Horse didn't give tuppence for Merseybeat music or *Pick of the Pops* – all he wanted was Elvis, shaggin' Elvis, and those corny flicks of his that were shown so often on Sunday afternoons in the Capitol. He was welcome to them. And those girls that squealed and gasped, 'Elvis, oh, Elvis' every time he grinned. He could have them too.

Horse knew that seeing him sitting there on the rock would bug us – that's why he was doing it.

Judo elbowed me.

'He shouldn't have his dirty arse on the rock,' he said.

'Why don't ya tell him that so,' I said.

I certainly wasn't going to say anything to Horse. It would only result in a thumping for me, and amusement for the others.

I looked round our camp, snug in its enclosure of thick bushes and trees beside the railway line. Our private world. Known only to us. There was a well-used look to it now: grass brown and trampled flat all around, edged by a rich green growth of thick scutch grass, tall nettles and a mixture of buachalainns and docks gone to seed. Jim had invented Indian symbols and painted them on the sacking of the teepees in red, yellow and blue.

I sat back for a moment, luxuriating in the knowledge that this place was exclusively ours. Our creation, even if it was only rough poles and old sacking. It was ours.

I returned my attention to Horse and Paudie. We were heading to the dump, they were saying, to collect bottles and whatever else we could find that might be useful to us.

It was Thursday, dump day. The day Johnny Cummins went round the town, his big piebald pulling a boxcart, drawing the contents of the town's dustbins to the dump on Jesuits' Walk. Not that many houses had dustbins. Few people on The Valley had one. We didn't. Having a dustbin was a luxury. Mostly only shops and well - to - do people had them.

Johnny would make his way slowly along the Main Street, the big iron-hooped wheels of his cart rattling and knocking on their well-greased axle. He kept his cart and the spokes of those wheels painted a shade of orange. The placid piebald plodded along on huge hairy hooves. Johnny, slightly stooped, walked at his head, gently coaxing him along. Never a sign of hurry on either.

'Let's ride out,' Horse said, waving an arm like John Wayne.

We took off. Out of the camp through the bushes, onto the railway line. Measuring our stride from sleeper to sleeper. Sliding on our backsides down the grassy embankment beside the bridge and landing into Kerry Street. Judo and I had often waited under that bridge just to hear the rumble and rattle of the train and carriages passing overhead. Along Kerry Street we ran, past the hammer and clang of Mick O'Riordan's smithy.

Going down The Valley we met a man hunting two fat pigs to the scales in McCarthy's yard to be weighed and bought for the Clover Meats factory in Waterford. They'd be brought to the railway station that evening and taken away in a wagon attached to the rear of a passenger train.

One of the pigs provided a diversion for us by bolting into the Plots. We joined in the chase, trying to head him off, laughing, whistling, shouting, as he flattened potato stalks, uprooted carrots and parsnips, trampled scallion beds.

Finally we got him back onto the road.

'The poor craythur'll be rashers in a couple o' days,' Mamie said from her half-door, 'is it any wonder he made a run for it?'

I watched him trotting off, all red eyes and disgruntled squealing, his little tail curled above his fat behind. Unaware that he was going to his doom, distraught at being driven away from his familiar world and squealing his objections all the way along The Valley. The chase around the Plots had been a comical distraction for us – a matter of life and death for him.

We resumed our journey to the dump.

Running across Jesuits' Walk we saw Johnny and the piebald turning in through the gate of the dump. The cart piled high with cardboard boxes.

And better still, there was no Paddy Cahill there to chase us away.

The dump was Paddy's domain. He guarded it jealously, didn't want anyone intruding, disturbing his handiwork. Especially not us. He'd arrive later with a sprong and shovel to lovingly tidy the loads that Johnny had tipped from his cart. Arrange all the rubbish into neat banks and tiers. Whenever he came on us rooting and disturbing his banks he'd roar like a maniac and chase us with the sprong. Paddy had never succeeded in catching any of us, and never would.

He'd called to our house one evening to see the mother.

'For God's sake, Missus, will ya keep control o' them young lads or they won't lave me with a thing in that dump,' he said.

'Is that right, Paddy?' the mother answered, a bit puzzled.

'Every Thursday 'tis the same story, they're in there rooting and robbing, so they are, I can't keep a thing with 'em,' Paddy moaned.

'Sure 'tis only the dump, Paddy,' the mother said.

'It don't matter, they shouldn't be in there feckin things,' Paddy answered.

We were sitting in the kitchen, listening. When he'd stalked off we began pucking one another, repeating what he'd said, 'they won't lave me with a thing in that dump' and dissolving into fits of laughter.

'What class of an aul' oddity is that fella, at all, sure isn't it only feckin rubbish after all?' the mother said.

That set us off again with the mother joining in.

We watched Johnny coax the piebald round, saw the britchen tighten against his hindquarters as he began backing the cart.

'Back away set, back away set,' Johnny murmured gently.

He removed the tailboard, drew a long bolt at the end of the shafts, put his shoulder to the box and began to heave, trying to get the cart to tip.

Horse and Paudie went to the other side of the cart and heaved with him.

'Yeer fine hardy chisellers, God bless ye,' Johnny said.

A few minutes later he was rattling out the gate and we were rooting happily.

First, we set some of the cardboard boxes aside – we could flatten them out into makeshift sleighs later on and go skimming down the grassy slopes of the railwayline embankment. Next we gathered bottles, as many as we could lay our hands on. Medicine bottles of all shapes, colours and sizes; lemonade bottles, old milk bottles, large and small Guinness bottles; baby Power bottles– one cider flagon. We put them into an old sack. But couldn't resist lining some up there and then just to have a few potshots with our catties. There were arguments over who'd smashed which bottle. The small brown medicine bottles were the hardest to hit and break.

Judo yelped when he found a plastic container with 'QUIX' written on it in large red letters. It was an empty washing-up liquid container. Those plastic Quix containers had only recently begun to appear in the dump. It hadn't taken long for us to improvise them into water pistols. Pliable plastic, a thin nozzle, filled with water and squeezed hard, they made a perfect water pistol with a thin stream and long trajectory. Judo ran to the stream that flowed parallel to Jesuits' Walk to fill it with water.

Just then Paddy came through the gate pushing a wheelbarrow.

'Ye little scuts, what are ye doing destroying all me bottles?' he shouted.

Horse and Paudie grabbed the sackful of bottles between them, we scrambled through the barbed wire fence into Henehan's field and were gone.

'Lave back that sack, what are ye feckin on me now, Jaysus Almighty look down on top o' me I can have nothing with ye, nothing, ye little dalteens, come back will ye.'

We scooted across Henehan's field and up the embankment to the stone-built railway bridge that carried trains over Jesuits' Walk. Looking back we saw Paddy who had come more than halfway across the field, before losing heart and giving up the chase. We watched him walk slowly back to his station in the dump. Like a defeated soldier in retreat. We cheered and jeered, just to torment him. He stopped, looked back, shook a vengeful fist in our direction. Letting us know there would be another day when we might not escape so easily. A day of reckoning. I could imagine the scowl on his long face, could almost feel the heat and the depth of his anger.

Later, when we knew Paddy had gone home to his dinner and the garden that was his pride and joy, we went back to reclaim the cardboard boxes that we'd set aside.

Smoke rose from the dump as we crossed to it through Henehan's field.

'The feckin aul' hoor's ghost,' Jim said.

Paddy had burned all of the boxes.

We stood for a while watching the grey ash flutter away on a soft, swirling breeze. Paddy had taken his revenge.

Nothing for it then but lug the bottles back to the camp to enjoy the sound of breaking glass and the rubbery twang of the gallabandies on our newly-made catapults. Kept well out of the sergeant's sight.

# 15

# Sultry Days

Days turned sultry in early July. Not a breath of air stirred; horseflies, silent, vicious bastards, bit into bare flesh, making you scratch the sting to an itchy lump. They were sweaty days in dead heat.

Consumed by a phantom thirst I longed for drinks I didn't have the money to buy. I imagined myself drinking bottles of O'Brien's lemonade, quickly, greedily, until it fizzed down my nose. But the thirst that I thought was slaked would return as keenly as ever to torment me all over again.

Arguments and disagreements arose out of nothing as we lazed among the teepees in the seclusion of the camp.

Once Judo glanced at Pony who was carving a dagger from a piece of wood. Just an aimless, idle glance away from the hazel rod he was paring into shape as an arrow for his bow.

'What are *you* gawking at?' Pony asked.

'Nothing.'

'Ya can't gawk at nothing.'

'I was just looking.'

'At what?'

'Nothing – for feck's sake, I told you.'

'At me, you were looking at me, weren't ya? Ya feckin well were, I suppose you think you can carve better than I can?'

'No, I never carve. Jaysus, Pony you know well I hate carving.'

'Then why are ya gawking at me carving?'

'I just looked, that's all Pony.'

'And don't be calling me Pony either, who said you could call me Pony?'

'Everybody calls you Pony.'

'Well *you* can't, not anymore, d'ya hear me?'

Pony was roaring now at the top of his voice. Angry out of all proportion.

'Cool it will ya,' Judo said.

'Don't shaggin well tell me to cool it ya blondy-headed bollix, I'll fucken well tear the head offa ya, so I will,' Pony roared.

He jumped up then and launched himself at Judo.

They rolled around on the flattened grass, grappling, each trying to get on top. Judo shouting muffled, strangulated protestations.

The rest of the gang gathered to watch. There were certain rules that had to be observed in fights: no punches to the head or face. No kicks or punches in the stomach or privates. No spitting into faces. You could punch on the back or the upper arms. And a hard punch on the upper arm or shoulder muscle was painful, really painful. Could even be agonizing. Mostly when we fought we just wrestled. If Judo could get on top of Pony and hold him flat on his back to the count of ten he would be the winner. We all knew that wouldn't happen. So we looked on half -interested, waiting for the inevitable 'I give up, I give up' call from Judo. Because Judo wasn't one for fighting.

And when Pony straddled Judo's chest and began demanding that he give up that seemed to be that. But simply holding Judo down to the count of ten and forcing him to submit wasn't enough to ease whatever was tormenting Pony that day. No, it seemed that only total humiliation would do that. He began demanding apologies for things that had happened weeks before. Things that no one but Pony remembered.

'That's not fair, you're only making things up,' Judo shouted, wriggling desperately, indignantly.

'Are you calling me a liar?' Pony demanded.

And he was off again. Obsessed with the notion that he was being denigrated. Interpreting every word from Judo's mouth as a slight that had to be rebutted with violence.

'I didn't say you were a liar,' Judo shouted.

He was flushed. There was the glint of rage in his eye and the set of his face.

'You fucken well did,' Pony shouted back.

And then spat in Judo's face.

This triggered a wild almost superhuman contortion in Judo. Judo who had never won, or showed any desire to win, a physical contest of any kind. And there were many such contests in our gang. Retreat and evasion was always Judo's most trusted tactic.

He arched his entire body upwards lifting Pony clear of the ground, then dropped suddenly to earth again and somehow brought his legs up and hooked them around Pony's head. And pulled backwards. In a flash the positions were reversed. Judo was now astride Pony. And the normally conciliatory Judo was

72

transformed into a raging, swearing maniac. He punched Pony over and over on the face. Shouting all the time.

'You bastard, you bastard, you fucken bastard what did I ever do to you?'

'Judo, Judo, stop, willya,' I called, catching hold of his arm in mid-swing.

Whereupon he turned his rage on me, began swinging punches in my direction.

'I did nothing on him, nothing, the bastard, the fucken bastard.'

I backed away. Behind him Pony got to his feet. His nose was bleeding, His lip was split. There was a mark over one eye. He was crying.

'Why wouldn't he leave me alone, the fucker, I done nothing on him,' Judo was saying.

The rage beginning to die.

'I'll get my big brother onto to you, so I will,' Pony was saying, with no great conviction. He was just trying to make himself feel better.

'Bring yer aul' fella and yer aul' wan too, and all yer fucken relations, ya bastard, I don't care,' Judo shouted after him as he retreated from the camp.

We stood awkwardly for a while unsure of what to say in the aftermath.

A subtle re-aligning of our attitude to Judo began to take place. I went back to my sixty-four pager, about a British commando unit of frogmen blowing up a German submarine base. But my eyes kept straying over the top of the page to scrutinise Judo. He was poking at the remnants of a fire with the makings of an arrow. Minutes passed.

'Hey, Judo,' Philly Landy said, eventually.

Judo looked up.

'I'll get my big brother to kill you, so I will ya blondy-headed bollix,' Philly said, standing up, mimicking Pony, tearful face and all.

Everybody laughed, including Judo. The tenseness gushed away.

A few days passed before Pony slunk back into the camp again.

The episode with Judo wasn't mentioned.

# 16

# Pick Of The Pops

Sunday had come. July was into its third week, school well forgotten, Kennedy a fading memory. The old people still talked about him, though, as they would of someone who had died. Going over and over the events of the four-day visit, finding consolation in many of the things that he'd said.

We were gathered at the camp where we'd made a circle of stones at the centre of the triangle formed by the three teepees. Sometimes we'd light fires there and sit around smoking the peace pipe, having powwows or councils or war, not saying anything that we hadn't said a hundred times before.

Mostly we'd talk about the other gangs in the town, especially the Patrick's Place gang. We didn't trust them, but weren't bothered about them on that Sunday afternoon, though. Sunday was for *Pick of the Pops* – something that we anticipated from one Sunday to the next, especially since the arrival of Judo's tranny.

The flaps of the teepees were tied back and some of the younger braves were inside reading comics. Horse wasn't around to boss us 'cos he'd gone to the flicks. Nobody else had gone that Sunday because it was only an Elvis film, *Girls, Girls, Girls*. One of those stupid flicks that we all hated. Except Horse. I could just picture him in the pit, hair slicked like Elvis, practically on his own, Trishy Skelly and her friend Bitsy Brennan, squealing from the middle section the minute Elvis appeared on the screen. Flashing one of his goofy, sideways grins. It was mostly older guys with brylcreemed hair who liked Elvis. We all preferred the frantic, exciting music that we heard sometimes on the radio. Belted out by new groups like the Beatles and the Animals, the Rolling Stones. Music that pulsed with energy, screamed at us that there was something happening, something going on.

And that Sunday afternoon we were on edge waiting to hear

them, waiting for four o'clock, when *Pick of the Pops* would start. Judo's tranny sat there on its special rock, like a monstrance on an altar that we'd all gather round when the signature tune started and Alan Freeman's voice boomed out.

The tranny was made of white plastic with chrome strips and the word BUSH done out in chrome lettering. The tuning dial was circular with hands like a clock and station names printed on a pinkish background. I begged Judo to let me tune it to the Light Programme.

'Ok,' he said, dismissively, as though he was bored with the task of tuning trannies, that it was really a job for an inferior. Like me.

Almost trembling with excitement, feeling I had been invested with some kind of special power to mediate, I moved the dial, with reverence, imagining invisible waves of sound speeding miraculously through the atmosphere from those distant, mysterious places listed on the plastic face of the dial, zooming down into this tranny on this rock in this quiet spot, entering our ears, our consciousness as words and music.

Sounds that moved us. Brought us to life.

I twirled the knob running the red indicator through the stations. Crackling, hissing, bursts of opera, peculiar BBC accents, strange distant voices in foreign languages, sepulchral noises, broke staccato fashion from the tranny. Finally I got it settled exactly on the Light Programme frequency, right where the sound was truest. I stood back. All was set for four o'clock.

Most of us were smeared with warpaint. Jim had brought his painting tin with its coloured blocks and a shard of broken mirror that he'd found in the town dump on Jesuits' Walk. He'd painted red and black circles around his own eyes and twisted some grey pigeon feathers into his blond hair.

Paudie was acting chief while Horse was at the flicks. He was wearing the head-dress that Horse had managed to wheedle from Jim Shine who'd gotten it in a parcel from cousins in America. Jim Shine said Horse had given him five shillings, a gun and holster plus a bundle of sixty-four pagers for it. Horse said that

75

was all lies sure you couldn't believe anything from that crowd below in Burke Street.

Judo and I were stripped to the waist, pieces torn from old shirts tucked into our shorts behind and in front, mimicking Indian breechcloths. Blue and white diagonal stripes painted across my chest and face, green and yellow on Judo's. We were sitting on the grass shaving the skin off thin strips of hazel for use as arrows. Judo was cursing as he tried to split the top of an arrow and slip a piece of feather in to make it look like a real Indian arrow.

'Feathers make 'em go farther and higher,' he said.

'Our Paudie shot one up into the clouds, when it came down the feather was wet,' I said.

That's what Paudie had said anyway.

Just then the signature tune for *Pick of the Pops* burst from the tranny. An electrifying charge of energy shot into the sleepy, Sunday atmosphere that hung over the camp. Awakening crows, blackbirds, thrushes, lifting them silently from bushes, trees, the roof of the station house, blowing them upwards, above our heads, swirling and dipping on a wave of sound, sending a mare and foal in a neighbouring field away in a hightailed canter, overwhelming the click of grasshoppers along the railway line.

'Hi, there, pop-pickers...'

Smooth, slick, suave: it was Alan Freeman.

'Who d'ya think'll be number one?' Judo asked.

'Gerry and the Pacemakers,' I said.

'Naw, I bet they're after dropping down,' Judo said.

The music pulsed, throbbed, brought us upright, sent a shock of anticipation through my body, creating vague expectations. We sat around the tranny, slugging our O'Brien's lemonade, slowly savouring the Flash bars that we'd saved for this moment. The lower numbers in the charts were played. Billy Fury was still there at number fourteen with 'When will you say I love you?' down from eight the previous week.

Billy sang, and we sang too. Roared, carried away by the music.

76

Judo had a photo of Billy. His song had been in the charts since the beginning of June, had gone to number six. Was on the way out, would be gone next week.

Following a song up the charts was deadly. It might come in at twenty and rise. Sometimes a record came straight in at number one. Mostly only the Beatles could do that, though. Sometimes it came in fairly low and slowly worked its way up to number one. Growing on you with repetition. All through the week you'd be wondering and speculating about what number your favourite song of the moment would be in the charts.

And reigning over all was Alan Freeman. I knew nothing about him, didn't even know what he looked like, he was just a booming, electrifying voice from the radio. A voice that I loved listening to. Everybody in the gang loved listening to him as he cranked up the excitement on those Sunday afternoons – making a drama of the highest new entry and the fastest climber. And the new releases that he thought would chart. I loved the way his voice boomed confidently out blending seamlessly with the music he was playing.

The Beatles came bursting from the tranny, an old hit dropped to number sixteen, in the charts since May.

I turned it up really loud.

'Sha na na na na na na...'

All of us knew the words to that one and roared along, living it, mimicking every nuance to the very last chord.

I sat back, letting the music flow into me, living the songs that I liked, songs about things that I'd never experienced but vaguely felt were somewhere in the offing, out there in the future: love, heartbreak, cheating, the lot. Wink Martindale came on followed by Ray Charles. I didn't really care for any of those. But I'd often seen the mother turn the radio up when Wink Martindale came on with 'Deck of Cards,' one of those talking songs, and she'd really sing along when Ray Charles was singing 'Take These Chains from my Heart.'

Then something happened, something exquisite, disturbing, painful, joyous all at the same time. Roy Orbison's voice came

77

wailing and trembling from the tranny, singing a new song 'I'm Falling' that had come in a few weeks back at number sixteen.

It had peaked at number nine and was on the way down now at number thirteen.

There was such an ache, such longing, in the way his voice soared and trembled. I felt myself being taken somewhere that I didn't understand, somewhere unmapped, unscripted. As the song began to fade I felt that my heart had been gouged apart by some terrible emotion.

The moment faded. Freeman went on to the next song a Freddie and the Dreamers number.

I'd seen them on *Pathe News*, Freddie was always acting the eejit, trying to be funny, when all I wanted was music. Then the Searchers came on singing 'Sweets for my Sweets.' We moved away from the dangerous, spirit-rending possibilities of Orbison to the safe and sunny pop of the Searchers. They were at number five. On the way up.

'Heading for the number one spot?' Freeman mused.

I sat up then, anticipating, hoping that Gerry and the Pacemakers were still at number one. But no, they'd dropped to number three, below Elvis at number two with 'Devil in Disguise.' This meant that Frank Ifield was at number one.

'I told ya,' Judo said.

I was disgusted, not liking either Elvis because of all those useless films I'd seen him in, or Frank Ifield, because of his corny yodeling.

Then it was all over. All right, stay bright, Freeman was saying, until next Sunday. There was the usual flatness for a while as the tranny fell silent, a vague feeling of disappointment, as the real sounds of the world around were heard once more, and seemed so inadequate for a time. We lingered for a while then wandered off home to the mother for supper.

# 17

# Evensong

We'd just finished our supper, were sitting around the kitchen. The radio on.

The Cliff Adams Singers crooning: 'Sing something simple as cares go by ...'

The sound oozed gloomily from the radio. Seeped into our souls, deadening the spirit. Sounding like the prelude to the end of the world. So lifeless and dull after the excitement of Freeman and *Pick of the Pops*. I could hardly raise myself enough to read the Indian book I'd gotten from the library.

'Tis time ye were going, ye don't want to be late for the devotions now, do ye?' the mother said, glancing at the clock.

Didn't want to be late? We just didn't want to be there at all.

But there wouldn't be much difference between the gloom of the Cliff Adams Singers and listening to Fr. Clifford intoning the Rosary followed by an endless litany of prayers and intercessions.

The mother was sewing a patch onto the seat of my short trousers. I *hated* the thought of wearing it with that bloody patch. But it was wear it or go without. Anyway I was probably due to inherit the trousers Jim was wearing at that moment. It wouldn't be long until he'd grown out of them.

'Willya talk to them Joey?' the mother said.

The father was dozing and snorting in our only armchair, the *News of the World* crumpled across his stomach.

He sat up.

'Come on now, shake yeerselves up let ye, well Mother o' God, would ya look at the cut of 'em, why didn't ye wash that paint offa yeer physogs, yeer like half-savages,' he said.

We'd washed our faces at the Judy near the cinema on the way home after *Pick of the Pops*. A quick wash it had been. Mostly we'd messed around, splashing and squirting one another with water.

We gathered around a basin of soapy water, quickly washed our faces. Then out the door and into the evening with us, stopping at Horse's, then Landy's. Bringing almost all of the gang together once more.

From Landy's we took off running, not because we were anxious to be on time for Fr. Clifford. Oh no. We just wanted to be running really fast when we reached Mom Mom Gunn's house so that we'd get quickly past her ancient terrier. He seemed to have some kind of set on us that turned him into a snarling savage every time we passed along the road. Mostly he spent his time stretched like a corpse outside Mom Mom's front door – and sometimes in the middle of the road, as lifeless as a bundle of rags. But somehow he always stirred miraculously to life when we came along and chased us as far as his bandy old legs would carry him. When his exertions were over he'd throw himself down once more to await our return. Our tactic that evening and always was to be running really hard and get well past him before he got into his stride.

When we reached the church it was gloomy inside.

Cool, even on a summer's evening. A few old women were scattered in the pews, worn faces hidden behind mantillas, lips whispering and lisping incessantly, fingers counting off their beads. Penny candles flickered and dripped before Blessed William, the martyr. The rosary went on and on, Fr. Clifford's voice echoing to the height of the ceiling, mournfully, leaning on the Hail in each Hail Mary: '*Hail* Mary full of Grace...'

We were almost comatose in the pews.

Ringo from the Patrick's Place gang was seated two pews in front of us. He brought us back to life with a silent, poisonous, fart. I noticed him tilting slightly to one side, and knew he was easing it out. Long seconds passed before he sank back on the pew. Soon the invisible poison was carried on a draught to our nostrils. Mingling with the smell of mothballs and TCP from Cissy Doyle to our left. Almost suffocating us in the hopeless atmosphere that pervaded the church. Distracting us from the monotony of the prayers and hymn singing. Ringo turned, grinned, winked at us. Horse shook his fist at him.

At the end of the Rosary Fr. Clifford recited the De Profundis: 'Out of the depths I cry to thee, oh God...'

And so doleful, so weary did he sound, that our misery was complete. It wasn't difficult to believe that he really *was* calling from the depths of a deep, dark pit. I felt that my soul or some inner part of me, was being slowly suffocated.

'*Tantum ergo sacramentum, veneremur cernui,*' the choir sang, raggedly, mournfully.

I watched the servers bring the thurible to Fr. Clifford, watched him spoon the incense into the bowl, saw the sweet-smelling smoke curl and disappear towards the dark corners and cornices of the ceiling overhead. And then the climax: he donned the cape, raised the monstrance, we bowed our heads.

After what seemed an eternity he began the Divine Praises: 'Blessed be God, Blessed be His Holy Name... '

And all the while we were shifting towards the edge of the pews, ready to bolt into the fresh evening air. Ringo got out ahead of us. We chased him as far as Bob Burn's corner on The Green before giving up. It was only a token kind of chase though, our hearts weren't really in it.

'Shag him, that hoor is incarnated,' said Horse.

Which was Horse's way of saying that he stank.

He turned and we followed him along Barrack Street and onto the Main Street. Two men came strolling slowly from Patrick's Place heading towards Lonergan's pub. When we got as far as the Bridge Bar at the lower end of the street someone was singing from the smoky depths of the bar:

'My feet are here on Broadway, this blessed harvest morn...'

I listened.

It was Philly Landy's father, home from London for his summer holiday. We'd seen him going in there after second Mass dressed in a royal blue suit and red tie. All the fathers working away in England wore suits like that, shiny and new. They'd always head for the pub and sing ballads and those weepy Mother Macree kind of songs when they were home and drunk. And they were often drunk. The singing coming from the depths of the pub seemed as dismal and empty to me as the singing of the Cliff Adams Singers and Fr. Clifford's sorrowful tones echoing into the dark spaces above the altar.

I turned away and ran to join the others on the parapet of the bridge, watching cinemagoers crossing. Keeping a bit away from the men sitting there, engaged in their evening ritual: passing time, gossiping, gawking, smoking, spitting into the river, a prelude to their Sunday night in the pub.

*Days of Wine and Roses* was the film showing, starring Jack Lemmon and Lee Remick. 'Over 18s only' it said on the billboard. I wondered what could be so terrible about the film

81

that only eighteen - year - olds could see it.

The foyer of the cinema glowed invitingly as daylight began to fade. Mary Shine smiled and was busy in the little shop, handing out chocolate bars, bottles of O'Brien's orange and packets of Perry crisps. Taking money. Giving people their change. Sometimes when the balcony doors swung open I could see lights with beams angled softly down along pink walls suffusing the inside of the cinema in an alluring half-light. It made me ache to be inside, waiting, feeling that tremor of excitement as the lights went down and the curtains rolled back. Ready to be taken to another world. Especially one meant to be seen only by eighteen-year-olds.

Courting couples strolled easily across the bridge, girls with hands crooked in the arms of their fellas, the fellas trying to look nonchalant, aware of ogling eyes.

Before going home I stood with Judo at the rear of the cinema. Listening, trying to figure out exactly what was forbidden about the film. All I could hear were booming voices, sudden, dramatic bursts of music. Leaving me more perplexed than ever.

'C'mon 'tis getting dark, the bats'll be coming out,' Judo said.

Later, lying on the brink of sleep, balanced precariously on the edge of the bed, a position I'd been nudged into by Paudie's constant arsing, I heard Philly Landy and Mickey Kearney pause outside our house as they passed home along the road. Peeping from the window I saw them under the streetlight, oblivious to swooping bat-shapes, singing fervently, faces upturned to the moon and the stars in the night sky:

'Goodybye Johnny dear and when you're far away...'

That was a Bridie Gallagher song.

'Fair fucks to ya Philly, boy, fair fucks to ya matey son,' I heard Mickey say, as they resumed their journey home.

Mickey had been in the trenches with the British Army during the Great War and sometimes said 'matey son' or, 'all right mate' for emphasis. Or 'Blighty' when he was talking about England.

'And don't forget where'er you go that you're an Irishman,' was the last fading sound I heard as I sank into sleep picturing them stopping and starting their way down The Valley.

# 18

# Fishing With The Father

It was Monday evening. The supper was over and we were all thrown in chairs around the kitchen. Annie, the old woman who lived next door had just left after begging 'a few grains o' sugar to sweeten me tay' from the mother. The father was on the car seat. His stockinged feet stretched out before him on the blackened concrete floor of the kitchen. Studying a betting docket. If he folded the docket and stuffed it into his top pocket we'd know it was a winner. More often than not he balled them in disgust, flung them into the fire with force. This evening, though, he folded the docket carefully and slipped it into his inside pocket. We eyed one another. It had to be a good one. If there was only a small amount coming off it he'd have had tomorrow's bet written out by now using the money off the docket to cover it. One of us would be detailed to take it to the betting office next day. But it looked as though he was going to handle this one himself so there had to be a lot coming off it.

I felt a little surge of delight. There was bound to be some dividend for us.

'There must be money coming off that one,' the mother said.

'Only getting me own back is all,' he said, airily enough for us to know for certain now that it was a winner.

He even put his arm around her, gave her an affectionate squeeze.

'C'mon, c'mon, what's keeping ye, we're heading down the river to do a bit of fishing,' he said, his after-work tiredness suddenly gone.

I loved it when he came suddenly to life like that, didn't seem so weary – but above all, I loved it when he roused us up too, enough to make us abandon what we were doing to go somewhere with him. And fishing down the river was one of our favourite things to do with him. It was an adventure.

A few minutes later we were hopping and skipping like the children of Hamelin as we followed him down the road to Horse's house. Paudie giving us disdainful looks, as if he was getting beyond all this kid's stuff. Going off with the father and all that. Still, he came along.

Calling for Harry, Horse's father, was part of our fishing ritual.

Harry backed horses too, so we had to wait while they studied the racing page with great care, compared the day's dockets and shared their betting wisdom. Piggott was a 'good thing,' so and so was a 'dead cert' in the three-thirty the following day at Lincoln or Market Rasen. Tommy somebody or another had 'lost his arse' on Piggott in the four-thirty at Ascot.

We went outside to play a few aces of handball against the gable end of the house while we waited.

Then it was on to Mrs. Mullins's house further out on the Grove road to collect the fishing equipment – a net, and a pair of bloomers that the father wore going into the water.

We began to quieten down as we made our way along the laneway that led to the river. Became tense with nervous anticipation.

We'd never been caught by the gamekeeper, but we knew that it was a possibility. It didn't bother us that we were poaching – we never thought of it in that way, never felt even a second's guilt: we were intent on helping the father thwart the gamekeeper, who was our enemy, along with the sergeant, Brother Virgilius, and sometimes the parish priest. They were always waiting and eager to punish us for doing things they thought we shouldn't do. Like poaching. When all we wanted was a tasty trout to eat.

'I don't know what the big deal is about, sure there's enough fish in that river to feed the shaggin five thousand,' the father would say.

What's the difference, he'd ask, between catching a fish with a rod and catching one with a net? None. Either way, they wind up on a frying pan, don't they? We don't make sport out of it, do we, and give all our time talking about it afterwards like all those fishermen going down the river with their baskets and waders and this kind of fly and that kind of fly and two or three rods to go with them? Sure all we want is a few fish for the supper and we'd be there for a week trying to catch enough for all of ye if we were to use only a rod and flies.

We were only vaguely aware of the estate owner as someone who motored around in an ancient Land Rover saluting people with a lordly wave. He lived in a world far removed from ours, was somebody with full and plenty trying to deny us a few trout from the river. Trout that were there in abundance.

And there was nothing more delicious than a freshly-caught trout pan-fried in butter by the mother: my mouth watered just thinking about it.

'Remember now, not a cook outa ye, we don't want that shaggin aul' Black and Tan catching us,' the father said when we got to the riverbank.

We'd already had a narrow shave with the gamekeeper in the wood on the first day of the holidays. In places like that we were always primed and ready for flight. The father had had a few narrow escapes with the gamekeeper himself from time to time when he'd been out at night lamping rabbits and foxes. We'd never been with him on those night expeditions. Nor did he ever tell us about them. It was Horse's father who hinted at what happened on those night-time excursions.

Evening was the best time to net the river, when the sun was sliding away towards the Galtees and long shadows were stretching across the fields. And the pools of water that we waded in were dark and cool and still. The water so opaque in the evening light that it was hard to see the fish. But we knew they were there. They were always there in those pools, you'd see them on sunny days, effortlessly arrowing through patches of sunlight. Singly, sometimes in twos and threes. Sometimes followed by streaming shoals of brickileens.

Now there were plopping sounds and dark rippling circlets on the surface every time a trout jumped to feed on the myriad of near-invisible insects that hovered over the surface of the pool.

The father posted two lookouts. Horse was sent downriver to a stile in a fence about a hundred yards away. Jim was sent back to the gate at the end of the lane that we'd followed down from the road.

A few minutes later the father stepped from behind some bushes wearing his fishing gear: an old pair of Mrs. Mullins's bloomers. He was dazzling white except for his arms neck and face. We were all wearing makeshift swimming togs. I wore a sleeveless jumper, legs shoved through the armholes and a large lump where the mother had pulled the neck-opening together. A piece of twine held it round my waist. Jim wore an old shirt with the arms pulled off and the collar turned down to cover his backside.

We waded into the water. Legs and feet shone white and faint beneath the surface. The stones underfoot were slippery with moss, some sharp-edged, others round. The father waded out to the deepest part at the far bank where the water reached to his armpits, pulling the net behind him as he went. I held the other end, taking care to keep it taut.

Harry stayed on the bank.

We drew the net slowly along the length of the pool. The father did a circle in the water bringing his end of the net round to meet mine, closing it, then drawing it quickly towards the bank. Fish were thrashing about on the surface of the water, desperately trying to do the impossible: escape the net.

Harry grabbed the net from the father and dragged it out onto the bank. The fish flapped and flapped when they were shaken from the net onto the grass. White bellied, grey backs speckled in red, pink gills opening hopelessly. We were merciless – we knew how to kill them and they were quickly despatched.

Just as we finished the killing Horse came running from downriver.

'Quick, quick, he's coming, he's nearly here, quick.'

'Jaysus Almighty, I wouldn't doubt the shaggin hoor, hide the fucken fish, quick, come on will ye,' the father said.

Harry threw the fish into a pile.

'Throw yeer clothes on top o'them, now,' he said.

The father gathered the net, waded into the water, sunk it with stones from the riverbed.

'Into the water with ye, come on, come on will ye, let on we're here having a swim.'

The father was agitated.

All of us plunged in, so frightened we hardly noticed the cold water closing over our warm bodies.

The net and the fish were well out of sight.

We began splashing one another jumping off the bank as if we had been at it for some time.

The gamekeeper arrived.

He was carrying a switch, kept tapping with it on his brown leather gaiters.

'What's going on here?' he asked.

'How are ya at all, sure can't ya see what's going on, ain't it a grand evening for a swim, you sir?' the father called out, in an almost mocking tone.

Galligan looked around suspiciously.

Saw the wet flattened grass and rushes. The heaped clothes.

Harry pulled out a pack of Woodbines. Lit up.

'Would ya like a drag boss?' he asked, proffering the Woodbines to Galligan.

Got a dirty look for his trouble.

Galligan studied us.

'You'd want to be keeping an eye on those young lads of yours,' he said to the father.

'What d'ya mean?' the father asked.

'They were trespassing in the wood a while back, you know well they shouldn't be running around in there, cutting timber,' Galligan said.

'Cutting timber me arse, sure what harm could young lads do to the flaming wood?' the father said.

'It's private property, there's a sign on the gate they went in that says trespassers will be prosecuted,' Galligan replied.

'Prosecuted me arse,' the father snorted, 'why would ya prosecute someone for being in a bloody wood.'

'They cut down timber and stole it, that's against the law.'

'What law, the fucken Penal Law, is it?'

'I'm just warning ye, if I catch any of them in the wood again it's the sergeant ye'll be dealing with,' Galligan said.

'The sergeant me arse,' the father said.

Galligan turned away and strode back the way he'd come.

When he was out of sight we left the water and were dressed in a flash. Harry sliced the fish open with an old razor blade and quickly gutted them, flinging the guts away into the surrounding rushes.

'Maybe the gamekeeper'll see that,' I said.

'He will in my arse, he'd want to get back here bloody fast if he's going to beat the scawl -crows to their supper,' Harry said.

We hadn't gone twenty yards when the hooded crows were coasting down onto the fish's innards.

Minutes later we were making our way back along the laneway to the road.

Carrying the wet net and nine beautiful trout hidden amongst green rushes in an old message bag.

'How many times, how many shaggin times am I after telling ye to watch out for that bloody aul' turncoat?' the father said.

'But he didn't catch us, Daddy,' Jim said.

'But the effer *saw* ye, didn't he, he knows ye were there, doesn't he?'

When we got to Harry's house the father gave him three of the trout.

A few minutes later the mother was melting butter on the pan. Soon the tantalizing aroma and the sizzling, spluttering sound of frying fish filled the kitchen.

All thought of Galligan faded as we tucked in to the tender pink meat and the crisply fried skin of the trout.

# 19

# Spikey Comes Home

The following evening Spikey arrived home. Back after two years in London. The first I saw of him was when he sauntered across the convent bridge. Long-stepping it, languid as you like, while we sat on the parapet with all the aul' fellas watching the cinemagoers pass by.

'Jaysus willya look,' Judo said.

I looked.

All the aul' fellas on the bridge looked.

And looked again.

I didn't recognise him at first, thought that the lead singer from one of those groups that we'd seen on *Pathe News*, the Swinging Blue Jeans maybe, had stepped from the cinema screen onto the street.

'Jaysus, is it Billy Fury?' I asked Judo.

'Billy Fury me arse, 'tis shaggin Spikey,' he answered.

And so it was.

His hair was blond. It had always been fair, but now it seemed really blond. And long, the longest I'd ever seen, even on one of those pop singers. He was long-stepping it onto the bridge on high-heeled, pointy-toed suede boots. A kind of strap across the instep. His legs, encased in drainpipe, stripey trousers, seemed to have gotten longer since I'd last seen him. The jacket he was wearing was short and tight, coming just to his hips. With cloth-covered buttons. And a suede collar, like a Beatle jacket. A long cigarette dangled from his lips. Everything about him seemed long, really, really long. He looked strange, exotic.

Judo and I slid from the parapet and ran to him.

'Howya Spikey?' I said.

'Jaysus, Spikey, you look like Billy J. Kramer,' Judo said.

He took the cigarette lazily between two long fingers.

'All right, then?'

There was a faint Cockney intonation. A bit like Tommy Steele.

'Jaysus, Spikey, where'd ya get all the gear?' Judo asked.

'Carnaby Street.'

*Carnaby Street.*

That's where all the pop stars and famous people in London went shopping. We'd seen it on *Pathe News*. I pictured Spikey strolling into some boutique, being taken for a pop star. Spikey, from our little town, who'd been the leader of our gang even though he wasn't from The Valley, parading like a pop star round Carnaby Street.

We walked on with him, Judo and I, across the bridge, past all the men, who were nudging one another, sniggering at Spikey. Someone wolfwhistled.

'FINE GIRL Y'ARE,' another roared.

Spikey ignored them, walked on with an aloof tilt to his jaw, as though they didn't exist, didn't matter, flicked his cigarette-end between two of them and into the river.

He stopped outside the Bridge Bar.

'I've got an urgent appointment here, with a blond lady in a black skirt,' he said.

He winked, disappeared inside.

I went home that night restless with excitement, spent long minutes before sleep came imagining days that lay ahead, days when I'd spend time with Spikey, listening as he told of his exotic life in London. I wanted to hear all about London, because that's where most of us would end up when we were finished at school. At least that's what people told us all the time.

'Sure ye'll all be taking the boat one of these days, heading off to London.'

I'd heard the men on the bridge sneering and making jokes about Spikey that evening after we'd first seen him. How he was dressed up like a 'quare,' a right looking nancy boy. How he was always a bit weird.

I couldn't understand why those men had such a set on Spikey.

I'd never noticed anything weird about him before he'd gone to work in London. He looked different now, for sure, with his long hair and modish clothes. And I wished that I could be like him, pictured myself walking along Carnaby Street in the latest mod gear.

Just like Spikey.

But Spikey was evasive when we asked about his life in London.

Apart from telling us that he worked in a pub in the West End. Hinting that lots of criminals and offbeat kind of people came in there.

'And the ladies, oh, the ladies, they go mad for me, can't get enough of me, know wha' I mean,' he said, with a little suggestive thrust of his pelvis.

Judo and I spent much time pondering the implications of Spikey's words.

I'd heard of the West End. It featured often in the *News of the World*, a paper that the father sometimes bought on Sundays.

'That fecker is as pale as a ghost, he's not up to any good over there, in that place,' the father said.

Spikey was rarely seen during daylight hours. Most of his activities took place in the evening. For the first couple of days Judo and I spent ages sitting on the cinema wall, hoping that we'd meet him. We waited in vain.

'That bollix is like Dracula, he only comes out of his coffin at night,' Judo said, disgusted.

His first sight of daylight usually came late in the afternoon when he stepped out his granny's door and sauntered across the bridge to the pubs. Just like all the home for a fortnight building workers. Except none of them could match Spikey's pop star looks.

More than once we saw him heading for the Furry Hill, each time with a different girl. Always a solicitous arm encircling their waists, a deep interest being shown in every word they said. Each girl receiving all of his attention. While they were with him.

'Look at him, how does that fecker do it?' Horse grumbled.

They followed him one evening, Horse and Paudie, when he'd gone to the Furry Hill once more. This time with Peggy Cleary. Horse had brought along a telescope that he'd got for Christmas. They'd been gone for ages while we waited at the camp and wondered what was going on.

Later, sitting round the fire, our shadows dancing on the teepees, Horse gave us the lurid details of what Spikey and Peggy had gotten up to: where Spikey's hand had disappeared to, how Peggy had moaned and groaned and bucked.

And then she'd done the same to Spikey.

'Jaysus,' Judo said.

I had only a sketchy grasp of the facts of life.

'Will she get a baby after that?' I asked.

'Shut up ya fool,' Jim said.

'But will she?'

'What she'll get is a right batin' from her aul' fella if he finds out she was up the Furry Hill with that Spikey,' Horse said.

He went on to educate me on what happens between men and women, gave me his version of how babies were made. Judo and the others chipped in with variations on what Horse was saying. I was astonished. To think that was how I was made. I spent that night before sleep revising my notion that the mother had found me a babe in the wood. And all the time it was the aul' fella who did it.

The morning after I was looking at Peggy Cleary in a different way as I stood beside her in the butcher's shop, sent by Ellie Power to get a chop for Pad's dinner. Waiting there, weather - talk going on around me, I threw furtive, sideward glances at Peggy. Remembering what Horse and Paudie had told of her and Spikey on the Furry Hill. She looked straight ahead. Flicking occasional knife-like glances in my direction.

She was waiting for me when I came out.

'What were ya gawking at me like that for, ya little oonshock?'

'I wasn't gawking at ya, I was only looking at the clock, Jaysus I thought they'd never stop talking about the feckin weather,' I said.

'The feckin clock was behind ya on d'other wall, ya gobdaw,' she said.

'Spikey was asking for ya,' I blurted out then, stupidly, without thinking.

'I'll guzzle ya, ya little cur, I'll tear that freckledy head offa ya, so I will, that fella is only a tramp,' she hissed, making a drive at me.

I took off down the street, faster than Foxy's jennet.

I kept well clear of her after that. And only saw Spikey occasionally as he sauntered to the pub. Or winked broadly at Judo and me as he escorted another girl to the Furry Hill. I was puzzled when I thought of all the girls Spikey had been with up the Furry Hill.

'If all those girls get babies for Spikey he'll be like one of those sheikhs in the Arabian Nights, won't he?' I said to Paudie one evening in the kitchen, when the mother had gone into the bedroom.

'Jaysus, willya shut up, willya,' he hissed, nodding frantically towards the bedroom.

Giving me such a kick on the ankle that I resolved never to mention Spikey or babies again.

# 20

# Horse Goes Girly

Maybe what he'd seen Spikey doing with Peggy Cleary started it, I don't know – but Horse suddenly went girly. Up until then girls had been objects of loathing to him. To all of us.

It was unthinkable that we would allow girls into the gang. Even let them come near us. There were strict divisions, they had their games – we had ours. They could play with their dolls and tea sets, bits of broken delph, mark out houses with stones, make daisychains, do what they wanted just as long as they didn't try to get into our camp. We were warriors, Apaches. For us it was just like in those Westerns: the women stayed at the ranch or in their teepees while the men went off on adventures.

And now Horse, the one who'd drummed it into us that anyone seen playing with girls was a cissy, had gone girly. It was strange to see our great chief suddenly acting goofy around girls. Well, around one particular girl.

A girl who'd come on holidays to Pat O'Brien's, just down the road from Horse's house. A girl called Moira McGuigan from somewhere up the country, somewhere really far away, Donegal maybe, or Cavan. Horse wasn't sure. Moira was different: her accent, the knowing way she carried herself and looked at boys, well, the older ones, like Horse and Paudie, made her stand out from the girls on The Valley that we barely noticed. She hung around with Pat's sister, Kathleen. They were both thirteen, giggled a lot and whispered to one another when Horse or Paudie were around. I didn't know how to interpret all that giggling – was it a signal that they liked Horse and Paudie – or were they simply having a laugh at them? Horse and Paudie seemed unsure as well.

Horse devised a strategy to attract Moira's attention. While pretending not to be interested at all. First of all, he took extra care of his Elvis quiff, putting on lots of Brylcreem to keep it standing.

Maybe that's what they were giggling at – the old-fashioned quiff. Still, Elvis was number two on *Pick of the Pops* with 'Devil in Disguise.' But, those girls didn't look or walk like angels to me. Even if Moira did in Horse's eyes.

Horse's strangest tactic though was walking up and down past O'Brien's house. Probably hoping that she'd come out just as he passed. Or would chance to look out a window, catch a glimpse of him. Maybe he was getting some kind of thrill from the notion that her eyes might be fixed on him as he walked by. He wouldn't do it alone, though. Someone had to walk with him.

Someone like me.

I couldn't figure out why he didn't do his walk-bys with Paudie. Maybe it was because he saw him as a threat. Which seemed stupid to me – weren't there two girls, one for each of them? I didn't know then that it wasn't as simple and clear-cut as that when it came to girls.

This nonchalant walking by usually took place in the evening when we were finished gallivanting for the day. Horse would make some excuse, collar me and slip away from the camp. Down we'd walk, past O'Brien's house, about turn, then pass it once again. Me annoyed and sulky because I'd been dragged away from something more interesting than parading up and down past O'Brien's front door. Like feckin sentries.

We had to pause after each passing for endless minutes while Horse studied the front of the house, staring long and hard at the door while I chafed, wanting to be at the camp, wanting to be anywhere, but there with Horse. He stared so long I began to think he must have x-ray vision, be able to see through the shaggin walls like Superman. Or have a magnetic gaze that would draw her out.

'What d'ya reckon, d'ya think she'd go to the flicks with me, will I chance asking her?' he'd say. In a kind of muse.

I never answered 'cos I knew he was really talking to himself. If I had dared suggest anything he would have clattered me.

95

My only purpose was to serve as some kind of silent support or decoy. The kind who would follow his orders unquestioningly, out of fear rather than loyalty. And keep his mouth shut.

When he'd posed the question about her going to the flicks with him for about the tenth time, I'd had enough.

'Why dontcha feckin well ask her,' I said, 'she's coming up The Valley now with Kathleen O'Brien.'

He jumped.

'What, well, oh Jaysus, why didn't ya tell me ya feckin gobshite,' he said, punching me on the shoulder for being so helpful.

'I just did,' I said, rubbing my shoulder.

'C'mon, c'mon willya, we'll walk towards them,' he said.

We walked towards them.

As we approached them Kathleen grabbed Moira's arm, clung to it, as though it was a life -buoy.

Moira elbowed her.

'Howya Moira?' Horse asked, in a peculiar kind of voice.

I looked at him, astonished.

His face was contorted into what I took to be a smile.

That must be Horse's version of Elvis's goofy grin, the one that makes girls squeal, I thought.

There were no squeals from the two girls.

If this is what girls do to fellas, I thought, I don't want any of it. And then there was all that kissing and other stuff that Horse and Paudie had told me about, all that baby-making carry-on.

'I'm going to find Judo, Horse,' I said, desperate to get away.

'You're going nowhere dope,' he said, grabbing me by the hair.

We stopped, about-turned once more.

The girls were now sitting daintily on a low wall opposite O'Brien's house. Gazing with great interest across the river.

At what? I wondered.

All I could see was the town wall and the ugly backs of the Main Street houses. But there was something about the set of their shoulders, the way they seemed to be holding themselves in

96

readiness for something, that made me think they weren't remotely interested in what lay across the river. They seemed to be aware of us without even looking round.

We walked back the way we'd come.

I could see Horse tensing.

'I'm going to stop this time, definitely,' he said.

To himself.

But he didn't.

We walked past with Horse doing his goofy grin once again.

'Hello, Horse,' the girls said.

In a kind of chorus.

A whinny of giggles sounding shortly after.

An image of Horse and Moira doing Spikey and Peggy Cleary on it up in the Furry Hill flashed briefly across my mind. I banished it in horror. We made one or two further walk-bys. After that the girls ran into the house.

'Goodbye, Horse,' they called, in a fit of giggles before disappearing indoors.

Horse did eventually ask Moira to go with him to the pictures. She accepted. He brought her to the middle section of the cinema. Keeping as far away as he could from where we were seated in the pit. The balcony would have been really remote from us but he didn't have the money for that. The middle it had to be. And he sat there beside her being pelted with sweet papers and orange peel. It was an old gangster picture about Al Capone with lots of machinegun fire and screeching tires.

Afterwards, at the camp, he'd told us that he'd put his arm around her, had got her to lie in. I heard him say how soft her hair was and how sweet it smelled.

Paudie snorted.

'You're getting to be like Spikey now,' he said. Scornfully.

Talk of soft, sweet-scented hair was enough for me. Too much. Horse had definitely gone girly.

'C'mon,' I said to Judo, 'let's go down to the bridge.'

'Naw,' he said, 'I want to hear all about Horse's courtin'.'

I knew Judo was hoping Horse would tell them about the baby-making stuff he tried with Moira. I figured, though, that if the build-up to asking her to come with him to the pictures was anything to go by, it would be a long time before Horse got around to the baby-making stuff.

I went on my own to the bridge that night.

Wondering if Horse would ever get wise.

Horse didn't have a chance to woo Moira any further: the day after she lay into him at the flicks her holiday ended and she was sent back to her home up the country.

Didn't even say goodbye to Horse.

# 21

# Going To The Library

'C'mon willya,' Judo said.

He was growing impatient. It was after four on Wednesday afternoon. In a hurry to get to the library we had run all the way from the camp to our house, rushing because we wanted to be finished by five, then get to a telly in time to see Fess Parker in *Davy Crockett, King of the Wild Frontier*. Only two episodes had been shown so far and already we were singing the theme song from the show:

'Born on a mountain-top in Tennessee,
Killed hisself a ba'ar when he only was three...'

I had to persuade Judo to come to the library with me because lately he'd been getting tired of reading books, ever since we'd taken to watching whatever was on telly at around half-five. After the library we'd have to find somewhere to watch *Davy Crockett*. If Mamie's brother wasn't fussing around the kitchen we could watch it over her half-door. Otherwise we'd have to sneak into Burke's or McCarthy's pub and hope that we weren't spotted until the programme had started. If we were caught coming through the door we'd have to turn around – if we weren't seen until after it had started we'd sit there looking so pitiful and downcast they wouldn't have the heart to put us out until it was over. If we failed to get in to a pub we'd head up to O'Shea's TV rental shop at full speed to watch without sound through the shop window.

The uncertainty about getting to a telly and the delay in getting to the library was making Judo irritable and could easily make him throw his head and take off.

I was rampaging around the kitchen, trying to find my second library book.

'*C'monnn*, won't one feckin book do ya?' Judo said.

'Will ya hurry up and don't be keeping the chap waiting,' the mother said.

I found it finally, in baby Tom's pram, scribbles all over the flyleaf.

'I have to call for Paddy Harney's books,' I said.

'We'll never feckin-well get there,' Judo said.

Paddy Harney was the contrariest man on The Valley. In the town, probably. I was going to be cautious with him. If he was asleep on his chair I didn't want to wake him and suffer for it. Even though I was calling for his library books there would be consequences if I disturbed him.

So I stepped carefully up to his half-door and peeped in.

Paddy was lying back in an armchair, hairy lumps of stuffing bulging through its torn fabric. Lower jaw dropped. False teeth jutting horribly.

My heart lurched. For a split second I thought I was looking at a corpse.

I stepped back, grimacing to Judo.

A peculiar snorting sound came suddenly from Paddy.

'Jaysus,' Judo said.

Paddy sat suddenly upright, teeth clicking back into place.

'Whaddya scobbing at, boy? Ha, trying to make a feck outa me, ha, grinning at me over me own dure, ha, well, no-one'll make a feck outa Paddy Harney, I'm too long on the road for two little whippersnappers the like o' ye,' he growled.

Judo pinched me sneakily, making me jump forward against the door.

'Whassup with ya, am I dealing with a fool or what?' Paddy said, 'and as for that gobdaw behind ya.'

He shook his head wearily.

'I'm just calling for yer books Paddy, I thought you were asleep, I didn't want to wake you,' I said.

'Didn't wanna wake me my arse, all ye young lads are the same, no consideration, not a bit, for yeer elders, sonsabitches, that's what ye are, all o' ye, sonsabitches.'

Paddy had worked for many years in New York. On the

subway. He pronounced lots of words with a peculiar half-American accent.

The father said he must have been washing the trains or greasing the wheels because if Paddy Harney was let anyway near the passengers they'd have to feckin-well close the subway down.

I watched him poking around, looking for his library books, shifting bits and pieces on the mound of papers, *Reader's Digests, True Detective* magazines, Gold Flake boxes, medicine bottles, saucers, stale bread, bean tins, water bucket, a shaving brush, a broken mirror, and a host of unidentifiable objects piled on the kitchen table. Papers, cigarette boxes slid to the floor and were trodden on as he searched.

Finally he found them in a tea chest beside the fire.

'I gotta goose to pluck with you, buddy,' he said ominously, as he brought them to me.

For months now I had been bringing him his cowboy books from the library. Usually twice a week. And never a penny for my trouble.

'What harm but the aul' fecker have plenty of it,' Mamie said, one day when I was feeling hard done by and had told her.

Everyone said Paddy had dry money – sure didn't the postman call every month or so with some kind of cheque from the States. According to Josie Barrett.

All that came my way was a grudging grunt of thanks.

I'd read one or two cowboy books, just to see why Paddy was so fascinated by them. Why he had such an appetite for gunslingers and poker games in saloons. From what I could see all cowboy books were more or less the same. I decided that when you got to your third you'd have forgotten what the first had been about. There was always a sheriff, a saloon, a poker game, a piano player, a livery barn, a telegraph office, a schoolmistress, a ranch, a bunkhouse, gunslingers, and a guy who comes drifting into the middle of it all and happens to be the fastest gun in the West.

How could Paddy possibly tell one from another?

So, I spent most of the time in the library browsing around and selecting my own books.

It was one of my favourite places, the library. Like the cinema, and Mamie's telly, it was the gateway to another world. All those hard-backed books, their plastic covering torn and jagged, dulled with a million fingerprints. Well-thumbed yellowing pages with all sorts of stains. Hundreds and hundreds of stories that dozens of readers had lost themselves in on winter's evenings in badly-lit kitchens. Eyes rushing on from page to page.

Sometimes I'd start into a Hardy Boys or a Billy Bunter book, intending to read a few pages as a sampler, but instead I'd keep reading on and on, drawn into the make-believe world of Bayport or Greyfriars. Hardly noticing the library emptying around me until Paddy McLellan began banging around with the business of closing. Having to decide, then, whether to check out the partially-read book or pick a new one.

I would usually grab the first two Westerns I came to for Paddy.

Now he was standing before me, a murderous look in his eyes, *Massacre at the Big T*, open in his hand. A black-edged fingernail pressed down on a tiny pencil-mark below the first letter of the title.

'You're after bringing this feckin book to me a second time,' he said, 'I'm sick of reading about *Massacray at the Big T*, I don't want to *see Massacray at the Big T* ever again, d'ya understand me now? If I do they'll be an even bigger massacray on The Valley, so look out for this mark, if ya see that mark on any book you'll know I have it read and don't feckin-well want to read it again.'

I'd brought him *Massacre at the Big T* three times already but I wasn't going to tell him that.

Until that Thursday it'd never seemed to matter that I sometimes brought him the same book twice. He never knew the difference, his face would light up, as much as it was possible for his bony aul' mug to light up, he'd whip his glasses out and get down to reading them straight away.

I felt Judo forcing his way in beside me at the door.

'Paddy,' he said.

I just knew that whatever Judo was going to say would annoy

102

Paddy even more.

'Any chance you'd give us a couple o' them *True Detective* comics, if yer finished with 'em like?' Judo asked.

Those *True Detective* magazines came to Paddy every couple of months in a parcel from somebody in The States. They were months old and dog-eared.

I was fascinated by them, wondered what kind of detective stories those pages held. There were always dramatic headlines and pictures on the front cover. The one I could see lying on the floor had a pouting blonde woman in a low-cut yellow dress on the cover, pointing a gun at the reader. A bold headline above her screamed: 'THE LOVE THAT KILLED THREE PEOPLE.'

'They're not comics, ya goddamn little gobshite,' Paddy snapped.

'Is there good stories in 'em,' Judo asked, 'what about that one there, "THE LOVE THAT KILLED THREE PEOPLE?'

'That's nothing, that's only a middling class of a murder story.'

Paddy paused, he was leaning on the half-door now, almost a glint in his dull eyes as he started talking, library books forgotten for the moment.

'There was a story in one o' them *True Detectives* about a guy over there in the States, out in the Mid-West...'

'Is that where the cowboys do be, and the Indians?' Judo asked.

'Cowboys me arse, you'd have a better chance of meeting a goddamn leprechaun strolling down that road puffing his pipe than you'd have o' meeting a real cowboy, or a feckin Indian for that matter, in the States. That's only all for the pictures. Now willya whisht and listen, willya? Where was I? Oh yeah, this guy drove a pickup along the interstate...'

'What's an interstate?' I asked.

'O Sweet Baby Jesus, what class of a ballavawn are ya, it's a big highway that connects one state to another, will ye just listen, will ye, and not be interrupting a good story, this guy, see, he drove a pickup...'

'What's a pickup?' Judo asked.

'Mother o' God d'ye know anything, it's a goddamn truck and

103

he'd pick up hitchhikers and take 'em to a cabin miles off the interstate, he'd cut them into pieces, put them into a big meat - mincer...'

'Would they be dead before he'd cut 'em up?' Judo asked.

Paddy gave him a look.

'Well, Holy Jaysus give me patience, is that allyawn trying to make a feck outa me, or what?' he asked, looking at me.

I kicked Judo on the ankle.

I'd never seen a pickup or a hitchhiker.

But one thing I had seen was Paddy Grant, the butcher, feeding meat into a mincer.

I'd heard enough.

'We'd better go so Paddy, or the library'll be closed, I'll keep an eye out for that mark,' I said.

'What's yeer hurry, I'm only getting to the good bit – how he made them into sausages, and all, oh, ho, I'm telling ye now, there's some right quare hawks over there in the States, oh, I'm the man that'll educate ye, so I am.'

We ran to the library on the Main Street.

Straightaway I went to the cowboy books. I was going to make sure I wouldn't be on the sharp end of Paddy's tongue. Finally, I came across one called *The Lone Star Ranger,* by Zane Grey. I read the blurbs and a few random pages. It was about Buck Duane, a cowboy who becomes a Texas Ranger. I was sure Paddy hadn't read it. That he'd like it. I'd brought him a book once before that had been about a Texas Ranger. Ever afterwards he'd mention Texas Rangers with reverence.

'Them Texas Rangers, they're the boys that can sort things out,' he'd say, 'no arsing around with them fellas, plug ya straight away, fill ya full o' lead, so they would.'

Judo appeared at my shoulder.

'C'mon willya, we better get going,' he said.

I grabbed a second Zane Grey book called *Bowdrie* and read the blurb:

'It was a name that brought the most hardened gunmen out in cold sweat. Chuck Bowdrie. He could have ridden the outlaw

104

trail, but the Texas Rangers recruited him rather than have to fight against him.'

Paddy would love it, I reckoned.

I checked them out and ran to Paddy's house.

He grabbed the books with a grunt and turned away to his fireside chair.

'Davy, Davy Crockett...' was sounding as we crept up to Mamie's half-door.

'Tis only starting,' Mamie said, the minute she sensed us at the door.

'Yeer ok, d'other fella is gone down to Jack Kenrick's for a haircut.'

We leaned on the rim of the half-door, eyes squinting at the telly in the far corner of the kitchen. Carried away to another adventure amongst the hills and lakes in the buckskin world of Tennessee.

Later, just after dark, the mother sent me to the Judy for a bucket of water. It was dark and I tried to get out of it because Jim had been telling me stories about Dracula and the curse of the undead. And there were no street lights. I crept along expecting to have every drop of blood sucked from my veins at any moment.

Paddy's half-door was still open – and there he was, hard at work, long-nailed finger guiding his eye slowly across the page. It was ten o'clock, I'd brought him his books at five and he was still labouring away, reading by the light of a poisonous old Tilly lamp sitting on the mantel over a couple of sods smoldering miserably in the grate. He was leaning forward, book tilted towards the lamplight, riding in his imagination across some starlit prairie or gunning down a cattle baron's gunslingers from Dodge City with Slim, or Zack, whatever the stranger who'd ridden in from nowhere was called. Paddy was sitting there, lost in the cowboy world of the book I had brought him from the library. Oblivious to the misery and chaos of his kitchen, oblivious to his aloneness and to me gazing in at him from the darkening world beyond his half-door.

# 22

# Comic World

It was Thursday. Comic day. Shortly after twelve. Judo and I were running, past the cinema, past Peggie Hanley on the convent bridge – clinking message bag in her hand, heading for the Bridge Bar. On we ran, past the nuns' laundry, past the church, no thought of genuflecting to gain indulgences today. Past Paddy Green standing in the doorway of his shop, right hand deep in his trousers pocket. Scratching. You'd see men doing that sometimes. As they stood around with nothing to do. Putting down the time. Looking up and down the street. Scratching vigourously.

We skirted round Luggy Leahy, on his way into Scully's hardware shop and licensed premises.

'Slow down ye little feckers, slow down will ye,' Luggy shouted.

But we ran on, heedless, one thing only on our minds: getting to Bert Newport's paper shop as quickly as possible. That week's comics would be in and I had a florin burning a hole in my pocket. I just wanted to get into the shop ahead of Judo. Ahead of everyone in our own gang, the Patrick's Place gang, the Burke Street gang, the Green gang. Everyone. Because there would be comics galore. All brightly coloured, newly printed, spotless. No dog ears, no food stains, no torn pages – all of the blemishes you'd get dealing in swaps. There would be *The Beano*, *The Dandy*, *The Beezer*, *The Topper*, and *The Victor*. And I wanted to be first to turn the pages of a pristine comic, inhale the inkscent off freshly opened pages. Untouched by grubby, nosepicking fingers.

I reached out, pulled on Judo's jumper, dragged him back. Just enough to gain an advantage, help me get ahead of him.

'Ya fecker,' he shouted.

Out the corner of my eye, as I slipped first through the shop door ahead of Judo, I glimpsed Luggy's swollen, be-pimpled nose pointing indignantly in my direction, was briefly aware of him looking after us, annoyed. He'd be giving out about us in Scully's over his small bottle.

But people only listened to Luggy to laugh at him.

And I didn't care about Luggy or his feelings. Not right then, anyway.

Even going through the door I still wasn't sure which comic I was going to buy. I was torn between *The Beano* with 'Dennis the Menace' and 'The Bash Street Kids' and *The Victor* with 'The Tough of the Track' and 'Wee Bandy.'

And then there was *The Dandy* with 'Desperate Dan' munching cow pie between his massive, stubbly jaws.

With a florin – worth two shillings – in my pocket, I could buy *The Beano* and *The Victor*, and get one and tuppence back in change. If Judo bought *The Topper* and *The Beezer* we could read about 'Beryl the Peril,' 'Ginger' and 'The Banana Bunch.' But I wasn't *that* keen on *The Topper* and *The Beezer* because they were bigger than other comics, were more like newspapers with pages that were hard to fold back. And then there was the lure of the sixty-four pager *Commando Comics*, full of action, always about the war between the Krauts and plucky British Tommies.

Decision time came as I arrived at the counter and stood looking up at Bert.

He was chatting to the Major. Across a stack of newspapers. About horseracing. A sacred and never-ending subject of conversation with almost everyone in the town.

I hesitated respectfully, waiting to be noticed. The conversation about horses continued.

Judo kicked me on the back of the leg, urging me to talk up.

'What's the sixty-four pager this week?' I asked Bert, timidly interrupting a statement from the Major about a horse called Arctic Storm.

The Major fixed an eye on me – horses were being talked about, I should know better than to interrupt. With a gently disapproving shake of his head Bert showed me that week's issue: *The Hounds of War.*

The cover sucked me in immediately: a German soldier restraining two slavering Alsatians on leads.

Price one shilling.

I was sold.

I caressed the florin in my pocket before parting with it to Bert. I pocketed my shilling change then turned to Judo.

'You buy *The Beano* and *The Victor* and we'll swop around,' I said.

On the street outside old Peter Hegarty had drawn up on his ass and cart. His sister, Mary Ellen seated at the off front corner of the cart, legs dangling, a cushion under her backside. This was their Thursday trip to town to buy *The Nationalist* – and presto for their hens at Josie Stapleton's.

I skimmed through the pages of *Hounds of War* as I waited for Judo.

Getting a preview.

Saw lots of square-jawed German faces. Lots of *KAPOWS* and *KABOOMS* blazing off the page in jagged word bubbles.

Judo came out carrying *The Beano* and *The Dandy*.

'Why didn't you get *The Victor?*' I asked, annoyed.

I wanted to read about Alf Tupper's clashes with Vic Mason and the footballing exploits of Gorgeous Gus.

'Why didn't *you* buy it?' he answered.

'I bought a sixty-four pager, it cost me a shilling,' I said.

'Yeah, well, I'm not letting you read my comics,' Judo said.

'Those two only cost you 8d,' I said.

'I only had one and tuppence, you have more money than me, you shoulda bought *The Victor* yourself if ya wanted it. Anyway, I don't like *The Victor*.'

I thought for a minute: If I bought *The Victor* I'd have 7d of my precious, remaining shilling left for sweets. The lure of Alf Tupper won. I ran in again and had to wait once more as Peter Hegarty gave out about the weather, saying that it was 'fierce close now after all the rain we had,' then went tracing back to a distant scorching summer of his youth when even the dogs couldn't 'stick the hate.'

On the way back to the camp we bought sherbets and liquorice black jacks at Lil McCarthy's. And the girl in Mrs. Ward's shop winked at us and asked who we were as she cut us a really thick slice off the block when we ordered a threepenny ice cream apiece.

'I think we're related,' she said, after I'd told her my name.

Then traced out some kind of connection that didn't interest me between her and the aul' fella. All I wanted was to start eating the ice cream and get reading the comics.

'We'll get a teepee for ourselves and have a secret scoff,' Judo said.

On Kerry Street, just as we were about to climb the embankment to the railway line who should come along but the sergeant. Slowly, on his big, black bike.

'Where are ye off to now, me boys?' he asked.

'We're going for a bit of a picnic, sergeant,' Judo said, eyes on the ground, not daring to look him in the face.

'I hope now, yeer not going to be walking on the railway line,' the sergeant said.

'No, sergeant, we won't sergeant,' I mumbled.

'Then what are ye doing up there?' he asked.

'Nothing, sergeant,' Judo said.

'Aren't ye great boys now for doing nothing? Yeer always arsing around doing nothing, aren't ye, how do ye manage it at all? Come down outa that and don't let me catch ye up there again,' he said.

We scrambled down and walked backed along Kerry Street towards The Valley.

The sergeant watched us for a minute or two before pedalling off.

'Effin aul' Black and Tan,' Judo said.

When he was well out of sight we ran back, climbed the embankment and made our way quickly to the camp.

I didn't want anyone getting the first of the sixty-four pager while I was catching up on Alf Tupper in *The Victor*. Couldn't bear the thought of Pony dribbling all over *Hounds of War*, leaving sticky snotballs on its crisp pages. So I shoved it out of sight under my sleeveless gansey.

Still, we had to keep driving Gerry and Frank away every time they tried to force their way in and get their hands on Judo's *Beano* or *Dandy*.

In the coolness of that teepee I entered the black and white streetscape inhabited by the 'Tough of the Track.' An unfamiliar world of city backstreets, railway bridges, canals, people queuing at bus stops. Alf, the underdog, always striving to overcome the odds stacked against him. On his way to a big race at the White City he'd be delayed trying to help someone in trouble. It could be an old lady whose handbag had been snatched – Alf would put it right. He'd be late arriving at the track, but only because he was helping someone. Not like the toffee-nosed athletes he was racing against. With their blazers and scarves. They'd travel to White City in cars, splashing puddle on old ladies along the way. And Alf would see it happening, 'Grrr Blimey!!' he'd say, and promise to teach them a lesson on the track. He would, of course, but not until the last minute, when he'd beat them to the line with his burly chest thrust out.

Outside, I could hear the others at play. Desultory voices, drifting lazily, sounds seeming to hang for long seconds in the heavy summer air: Horse (unscarred by his recent romantic endeavours) was talking with Paudie about the Beauties of Bath (they called them Beauty Bats) and pears reddening nicely in the Protestant minister's orchard, ripening for a raid; speculating about the upcoming Carnival, mostly about the amusements and when they'd be arriving. Jim and Philly were laughing, grunting, having a knife-fight using daggers they'd carved from wood. And Gerry and Frank whining at the tent flap:

'We want to come in, it's not fair, ye don't own the tents.'

'They're not tents, they're teepees,' Judo said.

'I'm telling on you,' Gerry said.

'Shag off, willya,' I said, not wanting to be drawn from my imaginary, comic world.

Suddenly, in the distance, from across the railway line, came the sound of Dick Gough's sire, Master Owen, squealing demonically. An in season mare had arrived.

'C'mon, c'mon, let's go for a gawk,' Horse called.

I heard them run off.

'Are ya coming,' Judo asked.

'Naw, I'm gonta read my sixty-four pager,' I said.

Judo, hesitated, then ran off to join the others on the fence overlooking the upright sleeper to which Master Owen's mares were tethered and hobbled while he did his covering work.

I opened the sixty-four pager and entered a world of square-jawed Germans: 'Schnell, Schnell, Donner und blitzen, Die Englander,' they shouted, bombarding plucky British Tommies with grenades shaped like potato-mashers, raking them with machinegun fire.

'Aargh, cop that Jerry,' the Tommies shouted back, or 'Fry Fritz' – balls of fire billowing from a flamethrower.

Shrieks from Master Owen and the unfortunate mare came and went, rose and fell, gained in intensity, muted by distance, kept on the margins of consciousness by my absorption in *Hounds of Hell*.

It was a calm summer's day, in the distance a mare was being violently possessed by Master Owen with all of the gang stretched on the bank of the railway line looking on. There in the teepee my imagination was possessed by comic-book scenes of murder and mayhem.

It seemed the most natural, un-troubling thing in the world.

# 23

# Feckin Apples

It was one of those dull, dispiriting sort of days. Sliabhnamon looking angry and purple, as if it had been beaten and bruised by something during the night. Heat from the sun coming through motionless banks of grey-white cloud. The kind of day when you'd just feel like lazing around. The kind of day when you'd be contrary and edgy, get on one another's nerves.

Paudie, Jim and I were loitering at the stile opposite our house waiting for Horse, Pony, Judo and the rest of the gang to arrive.

A thick mass of flies hummed around the coping of the wall opposite Pad Power's house. He'd just emptied his bucket into the jungle of tall thistles and nettles growing at the other side of the wall. Soon flies had descended in a black cloud to feast on what had lodged on the coping. Sometimes we'd walk along the rounded coping of that wall. You'd have to skip over the stained spots where the buckets were emptied every day. And be really, really careful not to lose your balance and fall into the revolting mess below.

We always emptied our bucket in the river. Pad was too old to make the walk over the stile and down the path that sloped steeply through giant nettles to the river. And nothing on earth would have coaxed me into emptying the buckets for him – it was enough to have to empty our own.

'What the feckin hell kept ye, we're waiting all the morning?' Jim said, tentatively.

'We had to do jobs for the aul' wan,' Horse said.

'Anyway,' he went on, 'we didn't ask ye to wait for us, did we?'

Jim stalled for a moment, realised the futility of arguing with Horse, then turned his attention to the job in hand.

We were planning a raid on McCarthy's orchard at the far side of the river. Situated to the rear of McCarthy's hotel and bar on the Main Street. It was an old orchard, with gnarled, mossy trees that left green stripes on our clothes. The mother gave out about that – she had to steep them for ages before she could scrub the stains out. The best trees with the most prized apples were quite close to a stable yard that ran upwards to the back door of the hotel. There was always a lingering suspicion that someone was watching from the windows up there at the back of the hotel, would appear suddenly from that door when we were in the trees filling our jumpers.

There were about twenty or so loose boxes in the stable yard, used by the Tipperary Hunt to stable horses during the winter months when the foxhunting season was in. They were empty at that time of year and the yard quiet. No horses' heads nodding over stable doors. Still, we studied the yard and the back of the hotel carefully. We didn't want to risk being caught.

McCarthys were undertakers as well as publicans and there was a two-storey stone building with a galvanised door where the hearse was garaged and coffins stored.

I'd often seen Bob Grace reversing the gleaming black hearse from that building. A scary -looking coffin in the back. Driving off to put some dead person into it – if there wasn't someone in it already.

In an effort to discourage us from raiding the orchard and drawing one or the other of the McCarthy sisters onto him the father often told us that if we were caught robbing apples we'd be put into a coffin and brought for a spin in the hearse. The connotations of this were too fearful to even think about. The mere sight of a coffin in the hearse was enough to frighten us and the threat had the desired effect.

Until the apples started to ripen in mid-July. And became an irresistible lure for us.

Then our mouths would water and we'd crave a taste of sweet juice on the tongue as we sat on the stile and gazed down at the ripening red fruit. The lure of the apples pushed our fear of the coffins into the background. The fear was still there, though,

113

making us hyper-alert when we got into the orchard.

We set off. Horse leading.

Down along the bank of the river we sneaked, crouched and furtive, water-hens scuttling through the rushes, dark shoals of brickileens streaming through the water. We slipped across the rounded sewerage pipe, where the water churned whitely, using the square blocks of concrete that secured it as stepping-stones. After flattening a path through the rushes on the far bank we came to a place where we could squeeze through the snowberry bushes and whitethorn that formed the boundary between the narrow riverbank and the orchard.

Here we stopped to survey the orchard once again.

It was divided in two by a stone wall. Into a small orchard and a big orchard. All of the best eating apples were at the far side of the wall in the big orchard and close to the yard in full view of the back windows of the hotel. Maybe aul' Nell was up there now inhaling grandly through her cigarette holder, surveying us through binoculars. Just waiting to pounce. It seemed a long way across the orchard, through clumps of tall nettles and buachalainns, to reach those sweet apples. Earlier, in the spring, pigs had been penned in the orchard, had spent days rooting and turning sods with their ugly snouts, leaving the ground treacherously uneven under a crop of long grass and vicious nettles.

It would be tricky ground to escape over.

We tightened our belts with our jumpers shoved inside to form a pouch for the apples. Like kangaroos. We'd be coming out big-bellied with apples.

All was quiet, nothing stirred.

Horse whispered to us.

'Remember, if we're caught it's every man for himself.'

With that he went quickly over the wall followed by Paudie.

Within minutes we were swarming in the trees, packing apples inside our jumpers. Occasionally I'd pause to take a leisurely bite or two from an apple. The tension had eased, now that we were in the trees and our attention was on the apples. Judo had opted to climb into a pear tree that rose high into the air. I could see him high up in the topmost branches and the dull whitey-grey sky above him. He was trying to reach the ripest pears at the end of light branches that were bending ominously under his weight.

Jaysus Judo, I thought, you'll be coming the fast way down if you're not careful.

Just then I heard a shout from the yard. Looked around. A man was coming down the steps from the back door of the hotel – a dog running ahead of him. A big dog, white, with black spots. Barking. For a split second, a terror-filled pause, everyone took in the sight of the man and the barking, bounding dog.

Then I was slithering down through the branches. Enduring a moment of utter panic as I became wedged in a forked branch with my big belly of apples. I tore my jumper from the belt, released the apples like a bomb cargo from the belly of a B57, gratefully felt myself slipping through, hitting the ground – only I was smack in the middle of a clump of nettles and buachalainns. Not feeling the stings, though. I was terrified, seeing that spotted hoor of a dog clearing the wall, slowing down, sliding a little when he landed on the soft slippery straw that lay on top of the dung heap. I sprinted for the low wall, crouching, saw Horse, Paudie, Jim, the rest of the gang vaulting over it with scarcely a break in stride, then Jaysus, I suddenly went sprawling over a hole left by a pig-snout, cursing I pulled myself upright, not even feeling the scratches from low branches on my arms and face.

I scrambled to my feet. At the low wall I paused, took a quick look back. And there was Judo tumbling down from branch to branch of the plum tree.

Flopping like a rag doll. Incredibily, when he hit the ground, he was already running, making for the wall where I stood roaring, 'C'mon Judo, c'mon!'

I ran on, turned again at the gap in the boundary ditch.

And there, poised on the wall, the spotted dog with the arse of his shorts between his teeth, a look of terror on his face, was Judo.

For a long frozen second I saw them, Judo straining forward,

115

the dog pulling backwards, then Judo's shorts ripped away, the dog fell backwards and Judo was over the wall and running towards me. He wasn't wearing underpants. Underwear was unheard of, an unimaginable luxury.

I made myself wait for him and we tumbled through the gap and into the river together, splashed our way to the far bank.

'Here boy, here, c'mon Rory, c'mon,' I heard a voice call.

The dog stopped at the water's edge and concentrated on barking furiously in our direction.

The man caught up with him there. Except he wasn't a man at all. He was probably aged about seventeen. He snipped a lead onto the dog's collar and took control of him. He waved to us with Judo's shorts dropped them on the ground and turned away.

'Did ya see that?' I asked Judo.

'Why didn't he call the fucker off sooner and I'd have me shorts in one piece?' he grumbled.

We were drenched, water squelching in our sandals.

'Jaysus, look, what am I gonta tell the mother?' Judo said a few minutes later, standing in his ripped shorts.

'Tell her ya got strung up on the branch of a tree,' I suggested.

He grunted.

We ran to join the rest of the gang on the low wall opposite the bank house and were so busy talking and re-creating what had happened that we didn't notice the Volkswagen approaching. Or the driver. With the cigarette holder gripped between her teeth.

The first warning we got was when she stepped into our midst and started cuffing Judo around the ears, then Horse. There was fresh panic and we were off again, this time running down The Valley, clearing the wall into Henehan's field, running towards Jesuits' Walk. But she had driven round to head us off in her beige Volkswagen and we had to swing right into Harrington's sandpit. We took refuge there, sitting around an old blockmaking machine and crawling into concrete pipes to amuse ourselves while she patrolled the road.

'Will that aul' rip ever shag off with herself?' Horse asked, in exasperation when she stopped for long minutes at the gate, looking in our direction.

Eventually she drove off and didn't come back. At last we were able to slink away home, wet and hungry.

Later, at around six o'clock, we went to the hotel and brazenly opened the door. It was time for *Rin Tin Tin and Rusty,* already we'd been turned away from Mamie Mackey's half-door. The Bridge Bar too. This would be our last chance to watch it with sound.

And there was Nell, just inside the door, sitting on a stool, trousered legs stretched out, cigarette holder between her fingers. I prepared for disappointment.

'Can we watch *Rin Tin Tin and Rusty* mam?' Judo asked.

She gazed at us from behind her glasses.

We turned to go.

'Go on, yeer all right,' she said, jerking her head towards the television.

# 24

# The Magnificent Seven

Whenever there was a film that we really wanted to see showing for the Sunday matinee at the Capitol we'd gobble the dinner off then take to mooning around the kitchen. Waiting, fretting, shifting about on the forms, sighing, moaning, watching the clock hands shift ever closer to two o'clock.

For at two o'clock Tom Shine would shoot back the bolts and throw open the double doors of the cinema. And we'd go sluicing onto the faded red carpet of the foyer. If we were there, that is. It was the worst feeling in the world, that sense of aloneness when you were left sitting on the wall outside the cinema, hope receding, dying, as everybody poured through those doors, entering that other, magical world. Except you. Left all alone and heartscalded, wallowing in self-pity. Knowing that all chance of getting in had passed.

And so the feeling that you could easily have missed out added an extra frisson of excitement to that rush into the foyer, the mad milling around the ticket office and the clattering run down the bare concrete stairs to the corridor that ran between unpainted block walls to the pit and the parterre.

That's where we'd wait and mess around until the film was about to begin. Elvis singing in the background 'It was a night, …' That song played over and over as we waited.

Most Sundays, though, we didn't have the money to go. Our own money, that is. I would will, mentally compel, the mother to find it somewhere: give it to us, please, please Mam, I'd silently beg. It was agonising, waiting like that, as the time for the matinee drew closer: doubts rising, wondering: will I be going? Oh, please Mam, please, find the money.

Really, desperately, wanting to go, not sure if it would happen.

And most Sundays the mother would somehow scrape the money together. Or part or most of it.

That's how it was on the second last Sunday in July when *The Magnificent Seven* was showing. Two weeks after Mamie had told us about it.

We had some money, but not enough. Paudie had enough. Jim had half. I had nothing. Once more we were watching the mother, willing her to go to the dresser, and please reach behind the rearing white horse ornament for your purse, perform another Sunday miracle, shake enough silver from it to get us all in.

But she was busy, tidying up after dinner, getting baby Tom to sleep. Listening to *Hospitals Requests* on the radio.

*The Magnificent Seven* had opened the previous Sunday night, had run for the entire week. Cars had parked all along our road. Never had I seen so many people going to the pictures. Every evening Judo and I had come down from the camp at half-seven to sit on the bridge and watch cars being parked, bicycles thrown against walls, people walking towards the cinema with a spring of anticipation in their steps. Then, when everyone was inside and the doors closed we'd run to the rear of the cinema and listen to the theme music booming out, listen to the sound of galloping hooves and endless shooting. Try to imagine the action. Eaten up with longing to be in there, part of it all. It seemed to me that Sunday afternoon would never come.

We'd wanted to go to the night showings but the mother had said we were all too young to be going to the pictures in the night time.

'I'm nearly fourteen, I'm old enough,' Paudie had protested.

'No you're not,' she'd said.

Anyway, she would never have scraped the money together to pay for us to go to the night showing.

Mamie Mackey had seen it twice.

'It's deadly, the best feckin cowboy film I ever seen,' she told Judo and me.

'Tell us Mamie, come on, tell us a bit about it, is there much shooting?' Judo had pleaded with her.

If there was lots of shooting it had to be good.

'The screen was so big with the Cinemascope, I was afraid I was going to be shot meself, or trampled be all the horses, or have me head cut off by one of them Mexicans with their machetes,' Mamie said.

We gaped at her, goggle-eyed.

'What's a machete, Mamie?' I asked.

'It's a big yoke, you could snag beet with it, 'twould take the head clane offa yer shoulders,' Mamie said.

'Feckin hell,' Judo said.

'What else, Mamie, what else?' I begged.

'Wait'll ye see James Coburn with his knife, he'd have ya stuck like a pig and dead before you'd know it,' she said.

'Oh, and Steve McQueen, the handsomest divil in Hollywood,' she added, wistfully.

Those snippets from Mamie made my longing for Sunday almost unbearable.

Now the moment was here and we were short on the price.

'I told ye to save up whatever coppers ye had,' the mother said, 'but ye wouldn't listen.'

'We had no coppers to save Mam,' Jim said.

'Oh hadn't ye now, and didn't I see ye eating sherbets yesterday?' she said.

'They were only tuppence each,' Jim said.

'Tuppence'd be a help now,' she said.

'Ah Mam, come on, please,' I said.

'Where do ye think I'm getting money from, d'ye think I'm making it?' she said.

I'd even cycled out to Mrs. Morrissey on the Grove road with a bag of crusts for her hens.

That was usually worth a threepenny bit. Except she wasn't there and I had to leave the bag on the doorstep with no threepenny bit for my trouble.

Finally she reached up towards the white horse. That was it, we were on our feet in a flash jostling around her.

'Deadly, Mam, deadly, thanks Mam,' we shouted, tension

released, excitement taking over.

She rooted about in her purse, counting.

'Ye have me heart broke and me purse empty,' she said, as she rooted.

'I've only two bob to spare,' she said then.

We counted up what we had between us. There were five of us going. There was only enough to pay for three.

'Gerry and Frank'll have to stay at home so,' Paudie said.

That brought instant howls from Gerry and Frank.

'All right, all right, they'll have to feck in so,' Paudie said.

We did that sometimes. The bigger ones would crowd round the teller's window while the two small ones ducked in as Peg Shine was distracted counting money and getting the tickets. They'd run to the toilets then and hide until the film was about to start and Cuckoo Walsh, torch-man and ticket-checker was gone from the door of the pit.

'C'mon, c'mon, we'll have to go, we'll be late,' Paudie said.

'For God's sake will ye mind ye don't get caught and make a show of me,' the mother called to us, as we got jammed in the front door, kicked and elbowed one another through it in our eagerness to get to the cinema.

Mamie was leaning on the half-door, fag in the hand, smiling as we rushed past.

'Mind the machetes, gringos,' she called after us.

Every boy in the town seemed to be swarming outside the cinema that Sunday afternoon. Judo was going from group to group. Tapping.

'I'm only short tuppence for the price of the flicks, how are ye fixed?' he asked.

'Shag off, Judo,' Horse said.

'Shaggin aul' meaner,' Judo answered.

'That shagger'll be drinking orange and eating crisps at half-time with all the tapping he's doing,' Horse said.

At last the doors were opened and there was such a crush and a queue that Gerry and Frank were able to feck in easily.

We were seated in the pit, up close to the screen. On hard,

arse-numbing, wooden seats. At last we saw Cuckoo climb the short flight of wooden steps, disappear behind the curtain. The lights went down, we heard the cranking of pulleys as Cuckoo began winding the curtains back. He wasn't quick enough, though, and the crowing cock that introduced *Pathe News* appeared on the folds of the slowly opening curtains. We booed and whistled, sent a hail of sweet-papers, crisp bags, apple- cores and orange-peel at the curtains.

'Cuckoo, Cuckoo,' sounded in a chorus.

Tom Shine, the manager, appeared at the pit door and lit us up with his torch.

There was a bit in the *Pathe News* that showed the Beatles singing 'From me to You' which caused an outbreak of clapping and singing. It died off though when something came on about the Queen. Some advertisements for Brylcreem, and Phoenix the bright beer followed. There was another outbreak of booing and whistling as Cuckoo mounted the stage yet again, this time to adjust the width of the screen.

Beside me Horse and Judo lit up the Boston cigarettes that they'd bought loose at Lil McCarthy's.

Then at last the blue beams from the projection room blazed out, cutting through the smoke-filled darkness above our heads, throwing the first images of *The Magnificent Seven* onto the screen: Yul Brynner's name in huge red lettering, a blinding blue sky, brown sunburnt earth, haystacks. And the theme music pounding, making us sit up expectantly on our hard seats. I was gone. Lost in a world of tough cowboy talk, manly camaraderie, quick draws, knife throwing, peasants swinging machetes, and endless shooting And moments that had me feeling sad: Bernardo, the gunslinger who'd become friendly with the children, being killed; Britt, sticking his switchblade in the ground as he dies.

When it ended we charged up the stairs and out into daylight. We, The Valley gang, made straight for the Abbey Rocks. There was an unspoken, almost telepathic, understanding between us when a film had really carried us away to another world: down The Valley we'd run past the creamery and into the Rocks to re-enact parts of the film. We weren't interested in what Horse called 'stupid aul' kissing flicks.' We wanted action only from beginning to end. And we'd gotten that in *The Magnificent Seven*.

When we got to the Rocks everyone wanted to be their own favourite one of the seven. Nobody wanted to be a Mexican peasant or one of the bandits. But somebody had to be, so there were rows, arguments, sulks, because all of us couldn't be one of the seven at the same time.

That evening the father had to come looking for us on his bike as darkness began to gather around the mounds and in the hollows of that rocky field.

'C'mon, home with ye now, yeer mother is wondering where ye are,' he called to us. Reluctantly we went. Even on the way home we'd stop to argue and fight as we re-enacted the hand-clapping, gunslinger scene between Yul Brynner and the young guy whose speed on the draw was being tested.

Bedtime came.

We couldn't stretch the day any further, finally had to part from it, let it slip away into the hazy world of sleep and memory.

# 25

# Ellie Calls

I was sitting in the kitchen. Reading. *The War Chief*, all about Geronimo, the Apache chief, when he was young and full of dreams. Mostly of being an Apache brave. Geronimo moved in my imagination and Ellie was in the kitchen having a chat with the mother. Only she was doing most of the talking, the mother listening. Sitting on the single Morris Minor car seat beside the fire, Ellie was keening away as always in her quavering voice.

She called in maybe once a week for a chat with the mother. Chatting for Ellie meant giving a long account of her gripes and grievances with her own world and everyone in it while the mother listened patiently.

'Indeed, missis, sure a body could hardly get out the door with that fella perched there with his elbows on the rim all day smoking and dribbling on that aul' pipe of his and he belching for sport and spitting like a feckin cuckoo,' she was saying.

'That fella' was Pad, her husband, a semi-invalid who bobbed around The Valley with a walking stick on account of his one short leg.

She'd always start the visit with a good long gripe about Pad.

Jim, who was sitting on the form opposite reading *Robinson Crusoe*, kicked me under the table. On the ankle. Rolled his eyes towards Ellie, trying to make me laugh.

'Sure, no one knows the life I have with that fella,' Ellie was saying, warming to her favourite theme, 'oh, he's a great fella when he's up around that town collecting his pension or in the pub cracking jokes and telling good ones, but when he's back in his own kitchen with porter in his belly, I'm telling you he can be a right sour aul' fecker, so he can.'

'Sure amn't I to be pitied,' she whined, looking to the mother for sympathy.

'Sure, haven't we our health,' the mother said, not having any real answer to Ellie's unrelenting pessimism and self-pity.

Mentioning health opened up another of Ellie's favourite topics.

'Health, is it? Don't talk to me about health willya, and me after getting a goiter down on top o' me hernia and ulster not to mention me varicose veins, and d'other fella filling the bucket to the brim every night with his water and he missing the feckin thing half the time, sure 'tis a churn we'd want in the corner of the room, God help us, and the same fella couldn't fire into it if 'twas as wide as the feckin eye on the Convent bridge. Aisy knowing he's looking for the blind pension. An' he going around with only an aul' shirt with a short tail on him and me telling him to wrap his shirt around d'other thing, if ya know what I mean missis, but d'ya think he'd listen to me, not on yer Nellie. And do ya think I'd get e'er a bit o' sympathy from that fella? No more than an aul' dog on the road. I'm telling ya missis, if I was to tell him this very minute I had to have a leg or something off he'd only say, "sure that's a thing o' nothing, that'll be fine Ellie, sure where would ya be if ya had a leg like mine – now is there any chance you'd pare that corn on me little toe, I'm tormented with the pain of it, sure that's men for you ain't it,' Ellie said.

I pictured Pad making his way to the bucket every night, up down, up down, on his uneven legs.

I caught Jim's eye. We were shaking, holding in the laughter, both of us thinking of Pad poised over the bucket, bare-arsed in his scutty little shirt.

Ellie was only warming up.

'And all the wind he do have, and he as thin as a herring, sure you'd wonder where it all comes from, and he going off every night like the the big German guns at Navarone, sure isn't wind an awful affliction, oh I'm telling ya now missis, if you only knew the half o' what I suffer.'

But we did know. Were never allowed forget.

Jim tilted sideways on the form, grimaced as if he was squeezing one off. We collapsed faces down on the table, shaking

125

in silent laughter.

The mother quietened us with a threatening look.

Pad spent a good part of every day looking over the half-door, endlessly paring tobacco off a plug, filling his pipe, striking matches off the reveal of the doorway where the sulphur burns had left a reddish brown patch. He could spit to the edge of the footpath at the far side of the road. And did, all day, every day. Didn't mind who was coming along. Stuck one on the gearcase of Miss Quinlan's bike one Sunday morning as she pedalled to second Mass in the Abbey.

When we were walking past his house we'd always cross to the path at the far side of the road. Anxious to avoid stepping on one of his gigantic coddles which would lie there drying on the tar until the rain washed them away. If they weren't carried away before that on rubber-wheeled, creamery-bound carts.

Sometimes, when we were out early weeding our plot, he'd pass through carrying a sheet of newspaper on his way to have his morning stool. Because of his short leg he couldn't climb through the ditch to the relative privacy of the next field. Every day he went to the same spot in the bottom corner of the plots. We'd see him back carefully in beside a patch of briars and squat amongst the scutch grass, thistles and buachalainns reading the piece of paper until he was ready to use it. On his way back to his station at the half-door he'd pause at our plot, pull out his pipe, cast a critical eye over our work as he went through the ritual of filling it.

'I'll tell ye something for nothing boys, ye'll never make gardeners,' he'd say, spitting in among the stalks where we were weeding. No danger he'd turn aside to spit.

'An I'll tell ye another thing, going to the corner beyand there is a chancy business, a fella could get the sting of a buck nettle or the tear of a briar on a very delicate part of his anatomy, if ye follow me drift.'

He'd strike matches, puff on the pipe. Suck. Spit. Dribble. Contemplate us, the stalks, the mountain.

'Sure, haven't we great facilities here boys, all the same?' he'd

126

say, 'sure there's nothing like a good aul' movement in the open air first thing in the morning.'

We'd stop work, listen idly, as we waited for him to move on.

'I'm telling ye now there's ne'er a tonic like a good movement first thing in the morning, gets all the poison outa the system. I read in the *Reader's Digest* that regular evacuation is better than going to any doctor.'

He repeated the phrase, savouring it:

'Regular evacuation – what d'ye think o' that lads, eh?' he said, triumphantly.

Pad was able to make knowledgeable pronouncements because of all the *Reader's Digests* he read. Ellie would fill her message bag with them at jumble sales in the Town Hall.

And he made sure to get the poison out of his system on a daily basis with his constant spitting and his regular evacuation in the bottom corner of the plots.

The mother was feeding goody to baby Tom as Ellie talked.

I was engrossed in Geronimo's pillaging and keeping an ear half-cocked to pick up whatever they were talking about. And trying not to let Jim distract me or make me laugh at the faces he was making.

'That's a grand child, God bless him,' Ellie said, 'have he a little cast in his eye, maybe, God bless the mark?'

'There's nothing wrong with that child's eyes,' the mother said, firmly.

'I was only saying now, I wasn't trying to be pass-remarkable, but sure no-one listens to an aul' one like me. Indeed I don't know how you rear all them boys, missis, I just don't know, sure I haven't a chick or a child – other than himself, o' course – an I haven't time to bless myself. But sure, there's more work with that fella than with ten childer,' Ellie said.

'Arra, they rear one another,' the mother said, 'sure they're off gallivantin' most of the time.'

'Sure they're right, the craythurs, they're only young the once,' Ellie said, sorrowfully.

'Sure they'll always come home when they're hungry,' the

mother said.

'No danger my aul' fella'd gallivant away and never come back, I'd be nice and cushy then with me widow's pension and no-one to be bothering me, farting around the place all day like an officer's horse after a feed of oats,' Ellie said, sighing.

The mother nodded sympathetically.

'D'ya know what missis, I'm thinking of putting in for the blind pension meself, sure you know yerself, I can't see a thing, sure I haven't a stim of sight in me right eye so I haven't, and I can see nothing at all with the other one. I ask ya now, how many times did ya see me trying to find me way to the shop with one o' Pad's aul' walking sticks, and rooting around in me purse not knowing a florin from a half-crown?'

I'd never noticed any problems relating to her purse when she was sending me to Jimmy Hanrahan's for messages. She never mistook a tanner for a thrupenny bit.

They went on talking – *Ellie* went on talking – ranging from one thing to another.

'Isn't it a fright all the people is going to England, sure they'll be no-one at all left in the town, all them men going off to Blighty and leaving their wives and childer.'

She lowered her voice, leaned significantly towards the mother.

'Didn't I hear that Mickey Doran is making the odd call to Joey Malone's wife, since he went away like, but sure, that wan was always a bit flighty in my book.'

'He's probably only giving her a bit of a helping hand,' the mother said.

'That's what I'd be afraid of,' Ellie said, 'I'm telling ya now, the like of that fella'd be giving wan like her a bit more than a helping hand.'

'Sure Joey comes home often,' the mother said.

'Faith and he'd want to be coming oftener,' Ellie said.

She moved on to Mary Croke, wondered how Paddy, her misfortunate brother put up with her at all, at all.

'He's a bit on the delicate side, the craythur,' the mother said.

'If he is itself there's nothing wrong with his swally, he's well able to guzzle the large bottles, I believe,' Ellie said.

Jim made a drinking and a belching motion, swayed a little on the seat.

'The poor aul' devil, sure he'd want something,' the mother said, giving Jim a disapproving look.

I nodded towards the mother, warning him.

'D'ya know what I'm gonta tell ya...' Ellie said, turning back to the mother, preparing to launch into another story.

'Lord, would ya look at the hour,' the mother said, 'I'd better start getting the dinner, himself'll be home soon.'

'Sure doesn't time fly when you're happy and enjoying yerself,' Ellie said.

'Jonno, you bring the baby for a walk in the pram, 'twill get him to sleep for a while.'

'I don't wanta Mam,' I said, not wanting to leave my Geronimo book.

'Gwan, off with ya now, Jim, you go with him,' she said.

'Ah Mam,' Jim said.

Ellie stood up to go.

'Don't bother making any tay now, on my account,' she said, 'you have enough to be doing with that tribe o' childer to look after, God help ya. Sure I'll see ya again next week, if I don't see you before,' she said, heading for the door.

She stepped outside the front door. Looked up and down The Valley.

'Sure ain't the mountain looking grand this evening, they must be after painting the Holy Year cross 'tis standing out so white and all up there,' she said.

'I thought she'd never go, the aul' rip, and I'm telling you there's not much wrong with that one's sight, the blind pension how are ya, sure I'd nearly want binoculars myself to see that feckin cross on the mountain,' the mother said.

# 26

# A Fair Day In Fethard

'Keep outa the fresh cowdung now, let ye, I don't want ye coming back here destroyed,' the mother warned us.

She was slicing and buttering brown bread for us at the kitchen table.

'And keep well back from the hindquarters o' them big bullocks, they're after being out on aftergrass and 'twill be gushing outa them, so stand well back, I'm telling ye now, or ye'll be destroyed.'

It was the third Tuesday of the month: fair day in Fethard. The day when The Square and the Main Street were taken over by cattle. Big, rank-smelling bullocks with wet, dung-plastered rear-ends – the rear-ends that the mother was cautioning us about. Long, swinging tails wet and heavy with fresh dung, horns like the steers we'd seen in Westerns. Wild-eyed, snorting beasts milling about but expertly controlled by drovers with long, well-worn cow sticks.

It was half-eight, we'd been late getting up, were wolfing the breakfast down, in a hurry to get out of the house and up to The Square. Early morning sunshine lit up the road outside, brightening our world, luring us out, increasing the excitement that boiled and bubbled inside of us. Made our kitchen seem dull and gloomy. There was going to be a lot of activity up on the Main Street, and we were anxious to be there, right in the middle of it.

Drovers, cattle-dealers, farmers would have been gathering since early morning while we were still under our blankets. Some buying, some selling, some simply gawking, drawn irresistibly from their quiet fields to join the fair day stir. Monitoring prices, chatting, gathering titbits of news and gossip, maybe even drinking a few large bottles or whiskeys in the pubs with a special fair day licence to open in the early morning for the occasion.

Selling food as well as drink for hungry drovers who'd been on the road for most of the night.

Farmers living in the hinterland of the town had it easy: only having to get up before the first light of morning, herd their cattle along a few miles of road and into The Square. Anxiously driving their animals along, wanting to have them on view in the prime spots around The Square. Rehearsing prices and bargaining strategies in their heads as they howed their animals into town with their drovers.

Those bringing cattle from further away, from other parts of the county and beyond, would have been droving their animals through much of the night to have them early on The Square.

For one wild, noisy Tuesday in the month Fethard became the centre of the farming world for miles and miles around. And because we were on our summer holidays we would be there in the middle of it all.

Paudie and Jim had finished breakfast before me, were heading for the door. Grabbing their ash switches in the porch. The evening before we'd gone out and cut them to use as cow sticks. There was always a chance that a farmer might want someone to hunt cattle along the road to his farm. Someone who could run quickly, head cattle off, keep them from running in through open gates.

'Wait for me, make them wait for me Mam,' I said, trying to gollop down tea and brown bread.

'Why can't we go, Mam, it's not fair,' Gerry said.

'Whisht, yeer too small, d'ye want to get trampled and scuttered on?' the mother said.

'Jonno can mind us, can't he?' Gerry asked.

I shook a fist at him.

The one thing I didn't want was the irritation of having to mind small ones, having to hold them by the hand and keep them out from under the hooves of cattle. Away from the gushing scutter. Instead of being able to dart here and there when I felt like it.

'Can't ye take yeer hour and wait for him?' the mother called after Paudie and Jim.

But no, they wouldn't. They were gone. And I had to rush after them, a half-eaten cut of bread in my hand. Cowstick in the other. Not wanting to be left behind. Wanting to arrive into the tumult of The Square at the same time as the others.

Mamie Mackey was leaning over her half-door as usual.

'Look out for the scutter,' she called as I ran past, not stopping for her.

I'd caught sight of the other two turning the corner at the Capitol, sprinting across the convent bridge. I dropped the bread, forced myself to run faster, wanting to catch up.

'Hey, young fella, young fella, stand there, stand there, turn them, Jaysus turn them willya, for feck's sake,' a farmer roared at me as I rounded the corner at the cinema.

He was herding four big, panting, mad-eyed, scuttering bullocks across the bridge, a boy about my age who must have been his son running ahead, trying to keep them from escaping into Kerry Street or down The Valley. I stood in the middle of the road, waved my arms.

'How, how,' I shouted, waving my stick.

They turned onto the Cashel road, skittering and slithering on their cloven hooves. Wetting the dry road with crooked trails of green. The farmer had probably sold them to a dealer, was bringing them to the pens at the railway station where they'd be held until the fair had finished then loaded onto cattle wagons and shipped off to the North Wall in Dublin. Probably from there on to some English city.

The cattle wagons had been lined up on a siding close to the pens since the evening before waiting for their cargo of steaming, bawling cattle.

Those bullocks would probably be on someone's plate by the end of the week.

There was little happening on the lower end of the Main Street as I made my way up past the church. Smoke and raucous babble came from the open doors of the pubs. Occasional parties herded and howed animals down the street: some heading for the pens at the railway station, others taking one or the other of the roads that led out of town, droving the cattle that they'd bought to farms out in the countryside.

Some shopkeepers had permanent iron railings fixed to the walls at either side of their shop windows to keep animals from pressing against the glass. Or scuttering on it. Others had timber railings that they hooked onto the walls early on the morning of the fair, or the evening before. All designed to keep the scuttering animals clear of walls, windows and front doors.

All along both sides of the street from the corner of the Provincial Bank and right around The Square there was bedlam. The fair was constantly moving, twisting, changing shape, like a vast living thing, absorbing men, boys, cattle, dogs, asses and carts, horses, then releasing them from the whole to become individuals again. Cattle bawled, drovers shouted, prodded animals with cowsticks, dealers wearing tan-coloured, green-stained boots bartered with farmers. A kind of walk-way that narrowed and widened spontaneously ran through the centre of the fair. Farmers, young boys, dogs moved up and down this irregular space, merging into the crowds that gathered in places around some animals as deals were struck, hands were spat on, intermediaries tried to reconcile differences.

I ran to where ponies were being bought and sold outside the Provincal Bank of Ireland. Mostly Connemaras. With long, flowing tails and manes. Long fringes hanging down their fine friendly faces. Prospective buyers ran hands along their flanks, down their legs. Forced their jaws apart, making them grin horribly as they looked at their teeth. Had them trotted up the Rocklow road towards the Dispensary and back again. Demurred, devalued, criticised, strove to have the asking price reduced. Walked away in disgust, came back again for one last try.

From outside the Munster and Leinster Bank came the demented wail of music, adding to the cacophony of sound rising from the fair. A man wearing a brown shop coat and tall hat was cranking a horse-drawn barrel organ with sidecar seats. A skinny monkey with a red collar round its neck and chain attached gazed wide-eyed and fearful from its perch on the man's shoulder. Held a tin cup in two hairy little paws. The horse stood with drooping, winkered head, impervious to the pre-programmed, windy wailing that came from the organ behind him. It was his lot to draw that instrument from fair to fair, to football and hurling matches. To anywhere, cross-roads, town square or field, that crowds gathered. With master and monkey seated on the side-car seats. In the spring I'd seen them doing their routine at the annual point-to-point out in Tullamaine. When the music stopped the man walked around cajoling the onlookers with well-rehearsed comments and asides while the monkey rattled the coins in the cup, extended it imploringly. A great cheer went up when the monkey peed and a damp patch slowly darkened down the back of the man's tan-coloured shop coat. Unperturbed he continued haranguing the onlookers. Many began to drift away rather than have the man and his monkey embarrass them into parting with money. The man began cranking once more. This time the monkey did a pitiful kind of dance on top of the organ sometimes getting tangled in the thin chain that hung from around his neck. Much to the amusement of the onlookers.

A commotion at the far side of The Square drew me in that direction. There I met Judo. A three-card trick man and his accomplice carrying a butterbox had set up for business outside O'Donnell's pub. Nobody knew at first that the fellow who lost and then won a lot was the card trickster's accomplice. He looked just like another countryman at the fair. Except he wasn't. The trickster wore a collarless shirt, a battered bowler hat pushed back onto his poll.

'Watch, watch the way he does it,' Judo said eagerly.

I watched him show the Queen of Hearts, shift the cards around on the butter box. Once, twice.

I elbowed Judo.

'It's that one,' I said, pointing to the middle card.

I was right. A dart of excitement went through me.

It was the only time.

'Now you see her, now you don't, find the lady, put yer money down and find the lady.'

He moved constantly only staying in one spot long enough to dupe maybe three or four. He always started by letting an accomplice or two win.

'Maybe we should practice that Jonno,' Judo said.

Little Tommy Dolan from the mountain came along. He'd just sold two heifers, was carrying a full message bag. Whiskey had made him reckless, made him abandon his mountainy-man's caution and cuteness. He found the Queen twice and won. The third time he lost.

'Double yer money,' the card man said, 'I'll give you a chance to double yer money.'

Tommy kept doubling. His pound notes were getting scarcer. I was astonished at the speed with which money changed hands. All green pound notes, crumpled and dropped on the box with growing unease by Tommy. Why, I wondered, was he throwing his money away when it was clear he didn't have a chance of winning.

'He has to try and win his money back,' Judo said.

Tommy was beginning to look desperate, his boozy palaver deserting him as he began to realise that he'd been duped.

'What about me money, yeer codding me, I have to buy calves, so I have, ye'll have to gimme back that money, call the guards some o' ye quick, call the sergeant.'

It was too late for that. The card trickster and maybe four others who'd been part of the game had lost themselves in the fair. Vanished. A crowd gathered round Tommy, partly sympathetic, mostly just glad that none of them had been the one so easily duped.

When the sergeant arrived the tricksters were long gone, someone had seen them cycling away from the town towards Clonmel.

'C'mon,' said Judo, 'we'll see if we can get to hunt some cattle.'

We wandered along the walk-way, stood close to where farmers were buying and selling.

I tried to look nonchalant, held my stick like a seasoned

135

drover, swung it effortlessly, tapped my toe-caps, slapping it off the side of my wellingtons, making it seem as though the cowstick was an extension of my hand.

The smell of cattle was overpowering. And scutter seemed to pour from them non-stop. Plop, plop, plop it went, rapidly, wetly. Gushing out from under their shitty tails. Splattering your legs and clothes if you were too close. There were liquid inches of the stuff under their hooves.

Judo spotted a farmer from Coolmoyne – we'd often seen him trotting gaily past our house on his way to the creamery further down The Valley.

He pulled a thick wad of banknotes from the inside pocket of his body coat. Began carefully counting notes into the hand of another farmer. I recognised the pound and the ten shilling notes. The others I'd never seen before. I had never seen so much money in one person's hand. Judo was able to name all of the notes.

'That's a fifty,' he said, nudging me.

A red twenty. A blue ten. A brown five.

'You sir, you sir,' Judo called to the farmer who'd bought, 'are ya looking for someone to hunt the cattle, meself and Jonno here, we can hunt cattle, we're well used to hunting 'em, aren't we Jonno?'

He looked at me. Then at Judo. Studied us briefly.

'Oh we are, you sir, so we are,' I said.

'Right,' the farmer said, 'c'mere to me 'till I be telling ye where to go.'

He'd bought four weanling bullocks. Light, lively animals with the lean look of the greyhound about them. My spirits sank a little. I could see we'd have a job keeping ahead of those lads on the road. Getting gates closed. Making sure they didn't break down anyone's boreen.

The farmer told us he didn't want to spend the evening busting his arse running around the countryside after bullocks. If we could get them straight home without any bother, or without running them ragged, they'd be something in it for us, he said, with a crafty wink.

All the way out into the countryside I speculated on what that 'something' would be.

Long hard days spent thinning beet and turnips only to be cajoled and cheated by wheedling farmers had taught me not to take their word for anything.

Ways were always found to devalue work done, justify not paying the price agreed.

But there was no agreement – only a vague suggestion that there would be 'something' in it for us.

Maybe a half-crown, I deluded myself.

As we trotted up the hill towards the railway bridge I could see down into the cattle pens and the bawling animals packed in there, barely able to move. Waiting to be shipped out on trains. There was a paddock too, full of cattle with numbers pasted on their backs.

The four bullocks trotted along snuffling and blowing. Hyper-reacting to every sound or movement in the ditch. Even a bird fluttering was enough to send the feckers hightailing it and scuttering along the road. We managed to keep control of them, me running ahead, shutting gates, standing at the top of un-gated boreens. Then running to get ahead of them again. By the time we got to the farmer's place I was sweating and exhausted. Swearing I'd never offer to hunt cattle again. And there was the walk back to town. If we scored, the walk back would be more bearable. We didn't though. Score.

The farmer arrived home in his Morris Minor a short time after we'd gotten the cattle into a small field behind the house that his strange-looking wife had shown us.

'I'll fix up with ye after first Mass on Sunday,' the farmer said.

'But we don't go to first Mass boss,' Judo said, 'can't ya fix up with us now?'

'Well ye better go next Sunday, if ye want to be paid,' the farmer said, and walked off towards the house where his wife hovered anxiously in the doorway. With what looked like a red tea cosy on her head. No offer of tea.

'Hungry aul' shagger,' I said as we walked down the lane

137

towards the road.

It was rough with deep potholes, a thick swathe of grass running along its centre.

'He had loadsa money in his pocket,' Judo said, 'I hope he chokes on his tay, the aul' bastard.'

'Better not, till after first Mass on Sunday,' I said.

It was a long walk back to town with no money to show for our labour. When we got back the fair was almost over. Runny cow dung lay like a green slick all along the street. The organ-grinder and his monkey were gone. Thick piles of horse-dung were all that remained of the Connemara ponies. Shopkeepers were washing cow dung off their barriers before storing them for next month's fair.

Smoke rolled like aery tumbleweed from open pub doors. The racket of too many voices talking together carried down the street. Judo and I listened outside Brett's pub as someone sang 'Tipperary so Far Away' in a high-pitched, nasal twang. Loud cheers followed when he sang a reprise of the last line:

'I'll nevermore roam, to my own native home, Tipperary so far away.'

Already John Sayers was sluicing the street with water, using a big, canvas-coloured hose attached to fire hydrants. A green frothy torrent flowed off the footpaths, gurgled along the gutters and into the storm drains.

We headed for Mamie's hoping to see *Rin Tin Tin and Rusty*.

Later, at home in the kitchen I opened a book and tried to read. It was no use. Images of the day whirled in my imagination overriding the story I was trying to follow. The hoarse bawling of cattle carried from the pens up at the railway station. The sound of fear and desperation. The sights and sounds, the smells of that strange place filling those animals with fear, making them low long and desperately for fields they would never see again, low to the heedless starry skies and surrounding darkness as the train that would bear them away forever sounded an eerie whistle as it came through the wood at Grove and up the incline to the railway station.

# 27

# A Haircut

The mother was rubbing Pomade into our hair, fine-combing our heads one after the other. I hated the feel of the fine comb grinding along my scalp. And all the while that feckin Jimmy Shand was on the radio torturing us with his bloody melodeon, seeming to play the same tune over and over again.

'You'll have to get that hair cut soon,' the mother said to Paudie, 'it's getting too long altogether.'

Paudie was secretly trying to cultivate a Beatles' hairstyle with fringe down in his eyes and hair curling out over his ears and up from his shirt collar.

'I don't want to Mam,' he said, 'I want to let my hair grow a bit.'

'A bit, is it?' she said, 'you're starting to look like one o' them potes.'

I wondered what a 'pote' looked like 'cos I'd never seen any of them around Fethard, and what was so bad about them and their hairstyles anyway?

'But Mam, everybody is letting their hair grow long, why can't I?' Paudie asked.

'We'll have to see what your father says, and anyway, you'll only go cross-eyed with a fringe hanging down over your eyes like them Beatles,' the mother answered.

'But he'll scalp me Mam,' Paudie said.

Paudie had managed to escape the last hair cutting session when the rest of us had been shorn like sheep. Shorn almost to a stubble at the back and sides and to a miserable fringe that you couldn't even grip with your fingers at the front.

Afterwards we looked like a set of big-eared child-convicts.

Paudie had been trying to disguise his thickening mop by dampening and flattening it down, then combing his fringe to one side when he was in the house where the father could see him. He'd started carrying a comb. When he was away from the house he'd stop at the first window and tease his fringe down to his eyebrows and coax the hair out onto his ears at the side. He'd shake his head then to see if it would swing the way John Lennon's did in the *Pathe News* clips when he was singing 'oooooooh' and making all the girls scream.

Paudie was beginning to look a second time at girls.

'Why would ya want to look like them stupid Beatles, anyway?' Horse, the dedicated Elvis fan had asked, scornfully.

'Drop dead, willya, Elvis is pre-historic,' Paudie had answered.

Sonny Darmody had the best Beatles' hairstyle in the town, his fringe coming down thick and long over his eyes. He'd always wait until people were seated in the cinema so that he could parade in front of them when he was going to his seat, sauntering in with his head of hair and his pointed-toe shoes.

'That fucken nancy boy,' Horse would say.

Sonny was constantly stopping at shop windows to check that his hair was in place and make minor adjustments with his comb. Sometimes Jim would sneak up behind him and mess it up and run. He'd have to keep out of Sonny's way for a while afterwards.

'Even Horse is letting his hair grow,' Paudie said.

'Don't mind him, he keeps it slicked with Brylcreen, like Elvis,' the mother said.

'I don't care, I'm not letting the father cut mine,' Paudie said.

'You're not going to have a choice,' the mother said.

'Don't say anything to him, Mam, please,' Paudie said.

Baby Tom squalled in the pram.

She sighed.

'Oh all right, I won't open me mouth, but he's going to notice it sooner or later, then the machine'll be pulled out in earnest,' she said.

There was a surprise in store for Paudie, for all of us, when the father came home from the pub. He lay back in the Morris Minor car seat stinking of porter and cigarettes. 'Paudie,' he said, 'our Padraigh, is after getting a job below in the county Cork.'

Paudie looked up from his library book.

The mother paused from her sewing.

'Sure he's not finished school yet,' she said, carefully.

'Arra, what's the use in him going back to that slaughterhouse for another year, all he'll be doing is passing the time 'til he's fourteen, and that's only a few months away, he may as well start serving his time now.'

Paudie was silent at the kitchen table, watching, listening as the father decided his future. Looking tense.

'Serving his time to what?' the mother asked.

'The bar trade – in a hotel in Youghal. I know a man whose son is a manager there,' he said, 'they're looking for a young lad to work in the bar.'

The mother looked doubtful.

''Tis a fine hotel, he'll have full bed and board.'

'When will he have to go?' the mother asked.

'A fortnight or so, he'll let me know what day.'

'What do you think Paudie?' the mother asked, coaxingly, 'sure 'twill be a grand clane job for you, better than mucking around with some farmer.'

'I dunno, Mam,' Paudie said.

'You'll be grand,' the mother said.

'And that hair of yours will have to be tidied up, you couldn't go anywhere like that, looking like a shaggin pote,' the father said.

'I don't wanta have my hair cut,' Paudie said, in desperation.

Next evening after dinner though, it happened. The father sat Paudie on a chair in the middle of the kitchen.

'Daddy, don't take too much off, willya please?' Paudie plucked up the courage to ask, almost in tears.

'Faith, I've only the one way o' cutting, all or nothing,' the father said.

It had taken Paudie a long time to grow his hair – in a few minutes it lay around his feet on the floor.

When it was over Paudie went out and sat on the stile opposite the house.

I followed him.

141

Mamie came to the half-door to smoke a Woodbine and have a gawk up and down The Valley.

'Begor now young Paudie, you have a right Yul Brynner style there,' she said.

'Feck off willya,' Paudie shouted, and ran down towards the river.

'He was trying to grow his hair long, Mamie, like the Beatles,' I said.

'Was he now, well them Beatles have all the youngsters gone cracked, with their long hair and their mad music. The way things are going we soon won't be able to tell the women from the men,' Mamie said.

'It's not fair, though, long hair isn't any harm, is it Mamie?' I asked.

'Sure, I suppose yer right alannah, God knows, but 'tis hard for aul' wans like me to get used to it.'

I followed Paudie along the riverbank. He was sitting under the big elm that towered over the river. Once I'd stood under it, my head tilted back, gazing at Paudie, waving and shouting from way, way up in its topmost branches.

His freshly shorn head gleamed whitely in the dull evening light.

He didn't speak.

Occasional plopping sounds came from the black river.

'There's loadsa trout in there,' I said.

He didn't answer.

'You know something, Jonno,' he said, finally.

I shrugged.

'I'm going to head for London the very minute I'm sixteen, away from this feckin dump,' he said.

'Maybe the mother and father wouldn't let you go to London,' I said.

'Who cares what they think, who cares anyway, the very minute I'm sixteen I'll be gone,' he said.

He was going to be fourteen at the end of July.

'Pakie O'Brien didn't go 'til he was seventeen,' I said.

142

'He had to mind his aul' wan on account o' there being no one else at home,' he said.

I couldn't imagine Paudie going off to London. Not yet anyway. He hadn't even left school.

'You'll be able to let your hair grow now, when you're in Youghal I mean, and buy mod clothes and all,' I said to Paudie later, as we lay in bed.

He didn't answer.

# 28

# A Working Interlude

I felt sure Paudie would be glad of the chance to finish with school and head off on an adventure to Youghal in the county Cork. That evening down on the riverbank he had been so emphatic that he wanted to get away. But now he didn't seem so sure. Not at home anyway. But when Horse and the rest of the gang were around he'd brag about how there was going to be no more school for him, he was getting away from this dump, leaving all you suckers behind. He'd have his own room, his own money to buy clothes, grow his hair long and everything.

'Long hair is dumb,' Horse said.

'Better than looking like stupid Elvis,' Paudie said.

'Elvis is the King,' Horse said.

'Yeah, King of useless flicks,' Paudie said.

'Anyway,' Horse said, 'I won't be hanging around with you dumb dumbs for much longer. There's talks of a job for me, only it'll be here at home, I won't have to emigrate to the arsehole of Cork like some.'

'Who'd give you a job,' Paudie said, stung, 'and why would you want to be hanging around here, for feck's sake? When I'm working I'll be able to save up the money to go to London.'

'I'll have a trade,' Horse said, 'what'll you be? Nothing only an aul' pint-puller.'

'A trade, what kind of a trade, you're only talking bullshit, you have no job, what is it, why won't ya tell us?' Paudie said.

'The aul' fella told me not to breathe a word to anyone, in case anybody'd get inside me and cut me cabbage, you have to be careful, you know.'

'Cut yer cabbage, hah, when you have no cabbage to cut,' Paudie said, with absolute scorn.

On and on it went until everybody grew tired of it.

Next day though we were all cycling off together to thin beet for a farmer about three miles outside the town.

Billy Fury had come storming into the charts at number seven with 'In Summer,' a new song.

It wasn't much of a song but the words kept echoing in my head, taunting me, as I crept along on hands and knees between drills of densely growing shoots of young beet. Thinning them back to one at intervals of a foot or so. Without even the slightest degree of enthusiasm. Thinking of all the things I could be doing if I wasn't in this bloody beet garden. Torturing myself.

The world of bows and arrows and Indian camps had been suspended for a whole week as we crawled up and down the beet garden under a baking sun.

'Aren't ye lucky tisn't raining,' Mamie said, when I stopped one evening on the way home and complained of being sunburned.

But I was too tired to stand talking to Mamie.

The drills were two hundred yards long. Stretched out before us, sloped upwards to a crest then fell away out of sight. On the first grubbing crawl towards the crest I had been preoccupied wondering how far the drills stretched beyond. My heart had sunk when I reached the crest and found another hundred yards or so to the other headland. We were working from right to left across the garden. Arrival at the left-hand side would signal freedom. There were a dozen of us thinning yet that ditch didn't seem to be getting any nearer. I'd stand on the headland gazing back in the direction from whence I'd come, postponing the moment when I'd have to drop to my knees and begin the snail-like crawl back once more. To my unwilling eye the garden seemed as vast and endless as the prairie out West where the buffalo roamed.

I tortured myself with fantasies of floating on the cool, spring water of the swimming hole at Newbridge. Slowly, ever so slowly, submerging my dusty aching body.

'Wake up willya, ya tool.'

That shout from Paudie would always dispel my fantasies. And he was inclined to shout a lot these days. Ever since he'd heard the news about going to Youghal by the sea.

Payment was by the drill. A kind of competition developed to see who would get the greatest number of drills done, thereby earning more money than any other beet-thinner.

Judo and I weren't interested in such exertions. We didn't mind being stragglers. As long as we made enough to have the price of the flicks on Sunday, and maybe some comics.

'How many drills are left now?' I would call, plaintively, to Paudie, as I lay on my back looking at the vast blueness overhead.

'How da fuck do I know, don't be annoying me with your stupid questions, who are ya going to annoy when I'm gone?' he'd roar.

Madder at me than he needed to be.

Occasionally we'd abandon the work to break the monotony. Begin pelting one another with hardened lumps of clay.

Mostly though, we just crawled. Minutes crawled. Hours crawled. Days crawled.

In the evenings we gathered at the camp but were too tired to make any kind of effort at being Indians.

Friday at noon we finally made it to the headland. The last drill was thinned. Paudie had driven himself like a demon and had thinned more drills than anyone else, just beating Horse.

It was important to him that he beat the Horse.

'Ya wouldn't have bet me only for I had a blood poisoned finger,' Horse said.

It wasn't a blood poisoned finger. He'd just got a prod from a thorn.

When I'd taken the sacking off my legs and realised the thinning was over a new energy flowed into my limbs.

The farmer came and inspected our work, walked up and down the garden.

'The hungry aul' effer is looking for doubles,' Judo said.

'He won't find any on my drills,' Paudie said.

He came back to us and moaned about the number of doubles, wanted to cut us three-pence on every drill.

'I'll pull up every head of beet in my drills if ya cut me,'

Paudie said.

We got our money.

The mother let me keep two shillings so I went to Bert Newport's and bought a sixty-four pager and a new Dell comic called *Rifleman*.

Making sure, though, to keep the price of Sunday's matinee.

# 29

# Last Stand At The Abbey Rocks

*'I'm* going to be Custer,' our Jim was saying.

'No you're not gonta be, I said it first, and anyway I'm older than you an' it's my gun,' Paudie said.

'Yeah, but you're gonta be gone next week, so ya are,' Jim said.

'So what, so feckin what?' Paudie said.

He didn't like being reminded that he'd be going to Youghal the following week. This would probably be his last time with us in the Abbey Rocks. Ever since hearing about the job he'd been losing his temper over things.

'Leave him alone, let ye, don't be at him,' the mother would say, with a cautionary shake of her head, whenever he flared up at home.

Paudie waved the cap gun he'd got for a long-ago Christmas. It wouldn't fire rolls of caps anymore because the spring was broken in the trigger. And anyway he didn't have money to buy caps. He just fanned the hammer with his hand and made gunfire noises with his mouth.

'C'mon will ye,' Paudie shouted, getting annoyed.

'Yeer going to be the Indians,' he said, ushering me and the younger gang members to a spot about twenty yards back from the hump where he was going to make his last stand, just as we'd seen Custer do in the flick at the Capitol.

'I'm gonta be Big Chief Sitting Bull,' Judo butted in.

Paudie took three younger ones and told them to lie down at his feet.

'Yeer supposed to be dead, like Custer's soldiers in the 7th Cavalry,' he said.

'Who's gonta be General Custard?' Philly Landy asked.

'Jesus, I am, ya gobdaw,' Paudie roared.

'Is this gonta be Custard's Last Stand so?' Philly asked.

'Just fucken lie down and pretend to be dead will ya, and it's not shaggin well 'Custard' it's 'Custer' ya gobdaw,' Paudie said.

The three lay down, Paudie struck a pose, legs spread, gun pointing at us Indians.

'Ok, ye can charge me now,' he shouted

'*I'm* supposed to say charge, *I'm* Big Chief Sitting Bull, you're Custard, you can't tell the Indians when to charge,' Judo said.

'Will ye come on will ye, ye shaggin eejits,' Paudie roared.

Judo solemnly raised the piece of alder with two crow's feathers attached that was to pass as Sitting Bull's lance, made a sweeping movement.

'Kill the yellowlegs,' he shouted.

The Indian warriors didn't move.

'Go will ye.'

'You're supposed to lead us,' Willie O'Brien said.

'I'm Chief shaggin Sitting Bull, chiefs don't charge,' Judo said.

'Sitting Bull did in the flick,' Willie answered.

'He didn't.'

'He did.'

'I'm telling ya, ya thick, Sitting Bull didn't feckin well charge,' Judo said.

'Jaysus will ye all just effin well charge will ye,' Paudie screamed from his hump, abandoning his heroic Custer stance.

This time all four of us charged screeching like mad things while Paudie made machine gun noises.

'Hey, hey, ye can't do that, ye can't shaggin well do that, yeer all supposed to be dead now, I shot ye,' he was shouting as we dragged him to the ground.

An argument started then over how many Indians Custer had killed before they got to him.

'Custer isn't going to be killed this time,' said Paudie, rewriting history for his own benefit, 'and he's not gonta be scalped either.'

'I'm hungry, I'm going home for me supper,' one of the dead soldiers piped up.

'You're shaggin well *dead.*' Paudie shouted.

'Yeah, an I'm shaggin well starving, as well,' said the dead soldier.

'OK, let's ride, Kemo Sabe,' said Judo, waving his two-feathered lance.

'Ye can't go home yet, the battle ain't over,' Paudie called after them.

The Indians charged off across the Abbey Rocks whooping and screeching, leaving Paudie fuming on his hump.

'C'mon, we may as well go too,' he growled at Jim and me.

We left the Abbey Rocks scene of so many Sunday afternoon re-enactments of the war between the Indian and the white man.

# 30

# Danger Man

John Lacey lived two doors down from us. In that row of two-roomed houses, between Mamie's and Josie's. Faded brown paint crinkling and curling off the front door, the only door that wasn't a half-door. Cement wash that he'd slapped on for the Corpus Christi procession in June lifting off the wall in scab-like patches.

The peak of his cap, the sleeves and pocket-flaps of his body coat had a dull, greasy sheen.

I didn't like him. Or his wild eyebrows, or his blackheaded nose.

I was wary of him.

If he was at home he'd always appear out when we were playing soccer. Or trying to play soccer. With a ball made of wrapped newspapers tightly tied with twine. He'd run among us when we were playing, a grown man, shouldering us, knocking us over in a kind of frenzy, always wanting to have the ball.

Soccer was new to us. We'd play it sometimes on the road outside our house when we weren't too busy being Apaches. Usually in the evening when we were finished gallivanting for the day.

Mostly we used to play football and hurling. On evenings when there were matches we'd go to the Barrack Field to watch, hoping there would be a fight. Sometimes there were lots of fights, especially if it was a hurling match. We'd watch in delight as spectators rushed onto the pitch and wrestled with players. Nobody ever seemed to get hurt. Not badly anyway. Just broken fingers and cuts and bruises.

Then one Sunday on *Pathe News* we'd seen clips of an English soccer team called Manchester United. In May they'd won a big cup final at Wembley. Wearing red jerseys, playing in front of a vast roaring crowd. The game of soccer had seemed so fast and glamorous. The players seemed so skilful and tricky, so different from the ponderous footballers in the Barrack Field, who seemed intent on clattering into one other all the time. Somehow, after that, the games in the Barrack Field hadn't the same appeal anymore.

Sometimes John Lacey would brag of his prowess as a footballer. That shower of fuckers over the club team know nothing about football, he'd say, sure if they did wouldn't they have me on it? One of the best footballers ever to pull up a britches in this town. Should have played for the county, so I should. If they gave me half a chance I'd have shown them, so I would.

'Oh, I'm telling ye now, I could fop points over from any angle, left or right, bury the ball in the net, 'twas all the friggin same to John Lacey,' he said.

But old Pad O'Shea said John Lacey was a useless fucker who wouldn't kick a soldier off his sister.

A while back he'd started asking me to do messages for him. He'd call me into his gloomy kitchen with its bare floor, butterbox, table and two chairs, a washstand with a basin, and his bike lying against the back wall. A slasher and fork tied along the crossbar. The tools of his trade. A man who scarted ditches.

'You're Lacey's aul' pet,' Judo said.

He'd send me down to Maher's for a single slice of ham. Or to Jimmy Hanrahan's with a cider bottle for paraffin oil, or maybe a couple of loose Woodbines. He'd always give me a couple of pence, sometimes even a threepenny bit.

'Come in, come in,' he'd say, when I got back with the messages.

I'd stand just inside the open door.

Then one day he closed the door. I was uneasy, didn't like being shut in with him. Especially when he started asking me about girls, and telling me about all the women he'd been great with. How he'd kissed them and how they'd all been mad about him.

'Let me feel 'em up, so they did, oh I was some boy for the

women, so I was,' he said.

I didn't know what that meant but didn't like the sound of it. Or the eager look on his face.

'Did ya ever see a girl's thing?' he asked.

I gawped at him, not sure what he meant but everything about him, his voice, his face, his stance, made me want to get out of that kitchen, quickly.

That look on his face frightened me.

'I better go, I have to do some jobs for the mother,' I said, backing towards the door.

'Howld on, howld on, wait now, wait till I give ya something for yourself,' he said.

I just wanted to be gone, to get out of that stinking place, was frightened of Lacey looming up on me, breathing strangely too, fast, wheezy.

'Tis all right,' I said, turning to open the door.

He grabbed hold of me then, from behind, pulled me tight against himself. And Jaysus he began thrusting against me, turned me round, pressed his horrible stubbly mouth down on mine. It felt like my face was being scrubbed with sandpaper.

He was muttering things, about how he'd look after me, give me money if I'd be like his girl in bed. He panted, whimpered, pulled at my shorts, moved me towards the bedroom door. I was weak, voiceless with fear. He took one hand away to slip his braces off his shoulders, reached for the bedroom door. I managed to wriggle free then, pulled the front door open and stumbled on rubbery legs out into fresh air and open space, down to the river I ran, not looking behind, terrified he might be following me. I didn't stop until I was well away from him, was certain that he hadn't come after me. I knelt on the riverbank, shaking.

'Mammy, Mammy,' I wailed to my puckered reflection on the surface of the river.

Gradually the tears subsided, my fear lessened. I walked along the river and came back onto the road at Mom Mom Gunn's. I made my way back up The Valley then sat on the stile directly opposite our front door, ready for instant flight if he should appear. After a while the mother came to the door and called me in. She wanted a bucket of water brought from the Judy.

But that would mean walking past Lacey's house.

'Can I wait till after, Mam?' I asked.

'I need the water now to get the dinner for your father,' she said.

'What's wrong with you?' she asked, looking closely at me.

'Nothing Mam.'

'There is, I can tell, what is it, what's on you at all, you're as white as a sheet?' she said.

'There's nothing wrong Mam, I swear, 'twas just Mom Mom Gunn's aul' dog, he went for me an' I thought he was going to ate me,' I said.

'Are ya sure now?' she asked.

'Yes Mam,' I said.

I could see she doubted what I was telling her.

'That aul' pest of a dog should be put down,' she said, shaking her head.

She looked at me again.

'What were ya doing, anyway, why aren't ya off with the rest of the lads?' she asked.

'I had to get a message for John Lacey,' I answered.

'Had ya now, well, listen to me now, keep away from that crackawley, d'ya hear me? I don't trust that fella, at all,' she said.

'He could give ya a threepenny bit or a tanner for doing a message,' I said.

'Never mind him and his threepenny bits or his tanners, keep well away from him – d'ya hear me now?'

'Yes Mam, I'll go for the water so Mam,' I said.

'And get yourself an ice cream at Mrs. Ward's,' she said, handing me a threepenny bit.

I stepped out the front door and there was Mamie leaning over her half-door.

'Hello, young fella,' she said.

Her smiling face and friendly voice reassured me. I stood there, looking at her, listening to her but not hearing what she

154

was saying, not caring what she was saying, just happy to hear the warmth in her voice.

I didn't tell her about John Lacey. I never told anybody about him or what he tried to do to me that day. I didn't have the language to talk about such things. To tell of the terror that had flooded through me in that kitchen. The mother, though, sensed that something had happened and would give me searching looks and ask if I was all right but I could never bring myself to tell her anything about it. I didn't know what exactly he would have done if he'd managed to get me to the bedroom, not having had any clear knowledge of such things then. But an animal fear had driven me to get away, to escape.

Those moments alone with him in that kitchen haunted me, would flash unexpectedly into my mind for a long time afterwards. I couldn't erase it from my memory. It faded eventually, but never really went away.

I'd see him often, still coming out to barge into our soccer games, or hauling his bike out the front door, looking at me whenever I passed him on the road, and I would always feel the same: fear, apprehension, an overwhelming desire to run, get far away from him. Even without seeing him I'd have a sudden fear that he was lurking somewhere nearby. Just out of sight. Waiting to grab me.

He became a kind of ghoul that ghosted through my summer.

I never did a message for him again. None of us did.

# 31

# Teddy Boys

We were sitting around the camp listening to Horse talking about the Carnival coming up on the following Sunday.

'There's gonta be Teddy Boys,' he was saying.

'Teddy Boys?'

I looked at Horse, astonished.

'Yeah, Jaysus, are ya deaf or what, there's a mystery train arriving from Waterford, it's gonta be full of Teddy Boys.'

Horse folded his arms, challenging anyone to contradict him.

'Who told ya that?'

'Luggy shaggin Leahy! Tom Ryan told me, who d'ya think?'

Tom Ryan was the station master's son – he'd know all right. Normally, though, he wouldn't have had anything to do with Horse or any of our gang. But it wouldn't have been safe to ask Horse any more questions about it.

Instead, I tried to visualise Waterford. I'd been there once when I was in fourth class. The furthest we'd ever been from home. Brother Andrew had taken us there by bus. To a Feis Cheoil. We'd sung 'Sliabhnamon' – and 'Kilcash' *as Gaeilge*.

All I could remember of Waterford was dirty grey water lapping in the harbour, and a lot of ships streaked with rust chained along the quays. And those tall sinister-looking cranes.

Just the place for Teddy Boys, I reckoned.

I'd seen Teddy Boys on *Pathe News*. In their leather jackets, slicked hair, drainpipe trousers, socks showing. Scowling faces. Swinging bicycle chains. Waving flick knives. They'd reef you with a razor blade as quick as they'd look at you.

They were always causing trouble, wrecking cinemas, breaking shop windows, especially at seaside resorts.

And now they were coming to Fethard, our town. For Carnival Sunday. On a mystery train.

We couldn't have been more stunned if we'd heard that Attila the Hun was coming to ransack the town.

'Don't mind that Ryan fella, sure what would the like o' them lads want around here,' the mother said, when I told her about the Teddy Boys, 'Sure aren't all them Teddy Boys over in England – how would they get to Waterford – and what the dickens would they want in this aul' town anyway?'

'They probably have their own Teddy Boys in Waterford, Mam, they wouldn't have to bring them over from England,' I said.

'Arra, there's none o' them lads in Ireland, they're peculiar to England. There might be a scatter of them above in Dublin, and anyway, aren't they gone outa fashion now?' the mother said, reassuringly.

I wasn't sure though.

There was just one more day left to the start of the Carnival. During that time we could talk of little else. We speculated madly on what might be coming our way. Wondered what we'd do if we were faced with Teddy Boys.

We talked about it incessantly, walked about filled with a nervous expectancy, tense as soldiers on the eve of a great battle.

# 32

# Carnival Sunday

'Finish that dinner let ye before ye set foot outside that door,' the mother was saying.

'We're going to be late Mam, we'll miss the start of the parade,' Jim said.

'Eat it up now, I'm warning ye,' the mother said.

'Ah come on Mam, please.'

'I'm telling ye now.'

'But Mam ...'

A loud knocking sounded on the front door.

'That's the lads now, calling for us, we have to go Mam.'

'Oh, go on so, off with ye, and no scutting out of ye now, mind.'

We were already halfway out the door.

Gerry and Frank following.

'I'm not minding them Mam...go back will ye, yeer not coming with us, yeer to go with the mother,' I said to them.

'No, no we want to go with ye, tell 'em to bring us Mammy, tell 'em.'

I didn't want to be stuck trying to mind them in the Carnival crowds that would throng the town.

'What if ye meet a Teddy Boy with a big flick knife, ready to let yeer guts out on the ground, ha, what'll ye do then?' I asked.

'Mammy!'

'Don't be trying to frighten them, willya, look, ye better come with me, lads, I'll put ye on the swinging boats and the Chairoplanes,' the mother said.

'Can we get ice cream too, and a go on the bumpers?' Gerry asked.

'We'll see, we'll see.'

I was gone in a flash.

Out the door to join the rest of the gang.

It had come, finally, the last Sunday in July, Carnival Sunday, the air all around seeming to crackle and fizz with a dozen different irresistible sounds – full of promise, full of magic.

The Parade was the highlight of Carnival Sunday. Of the summer, almost. Entrants from all of the neighbouring towns and surrounding countryside gathered outside the Capitol cinema and paraded to the Barrack Field led by a band. There to be scrutinised by judges, have prizes awarded. Large crowds of people lined the streets and flooded into the field to enjoy the amusements.

I stepped out onto The Valley just as a sudden, electrifying blast of trumpets, trombones and big drum sounded. Stopped me dead in my tracks. For an instant we paused, looked at one another.

'Fucken deadly,' Jim roared, and we were off.

A lightning charge of excitement surging through us as we ran.

'Take yeer time ye little divils,' Ellie called, as we charged past her door.

And then we were in the midst of it all, colour and noise everywhere, bunting overhead, strung from pole to pole, flapping, bright and flaming, reds, blues, greens. People sitting along both parapets of the convent bridge, happy, lost in the pleasure of the day, the grey mass of the Presentation Convent rising behind and above them. Josie Barrett had told me once that there was always a nun standing at one of those gleaming windows in gloomy black habit watching everything that went on.

'Keeping an eye on little divils like ye,' she'd said.

A hawker carrying a basket full of ice cream tubs, fruit and chocolate went by, loudly advertising his wares.

'Anyone now for the last few tubs… get yeer tubs of ice cream now,' he shouted, over and over.

The sergeant strode importantly across the bridge, baton holstered on his hip, bestowing occasional nods of recognition as he went. The parish priest was moving about too, grim and black in long soutane and biretta.

People drifted, shifted, space opening up wherever either of them went.

Whenever they came too close Judo and I moved quickly out of their shadow.

A two-toned Ford Consul swept onto the bridge, a voice echoing from a loudspeaker on its roof, telling entrants where to queue: tractors, trailers and trucks – he called them floats – were to assemble along the Cashel road. Children's entries down The Valley and all animal entries, ponies and asses, and those on bikes or motorbikes along Kerry Street. Judo and I darted over to see the tractors and trucks on the Cashel road.

People were streaming down from the railway station: the mystery train had arrived. Women pushing prams, holding small ones by the hand, joined the crowds already moving and milling about. A man passed by: 'A Feathered Man From Carrick' scrawled roughly on the brown cardboard sign tied to his back. On a trailer men from the tennis club sporting striped jackets, boater hats, and blackened faces were crooning: 'Cruising down the river, on a Sunday afternoon.......'

No recognizable Teddy Boys were to be seen. Just a few bullet-headed boys with pale, pimply faces wearing leather jackets. Nobody paid them any attention. Apart from Judo and I. Feeling a mixture of relief and disappointment now that no real Teddy Boys had arrived. There would be no extra excitement, no riots or windows broken. The sergeant wouldn't have to draw his baton, call in reinforcements. Secretly I'd been hoping that a couple of Teddy Boys might give him a lash of a bicycle chain. Knock him back on his fat Kerry arse. I couldn't forgive him for destroying our catapults that day down by the river.

'They're probably up from Carrick, or out from Clonmel,' Horse said, when we pointed out the bullet-heads.

We watched for a while as they made cigarettes with a little roller gadget, lit up and rambled off into the crowd on Main Street.

The organisers were trying to get a group of ten or more horses and ponies – all wild manes and flowing tails – into position, arguing over whether they should lead the parade or not.

160

The riders dressed as Indians, boys with bare torsos painted in reds and yellows, girls wearing old waistcoats and makeshift breechclouts. Leading them was Evie wearing an Indian chief's headdress and a buckskin jacket, like Kit Carson, the U.S. Army scout. She made her palomino rear dramatically, pedal his front legs. Onlookers cheered, women grabbed small children fearful of flying hooves.

I gazed at those riders, mouth open, imagining myself up there, plunging and sweeping on horseback, Geronimo, the last free Apache, throwing an imperious eye on everybody and everything. Not the Geronimo that I remembered from the Indian book I'd read, the one who'd become a fairground attraction at the World's Fair in Chicago. No, I'd be the Geronimo who could run fifty miles across the desert and not leave a footprint. The Geronimo who …

'What d'ya think of the horses, young fella?' a voice sounded in my ear.

A voice that made me want to curl up like a hedgehog. The voice of John Lacey. I could smell him: that greasy, sickly smell.

'C'mon, c'mon willya the parade is starting.'

It was Judo, my savior, dragging at my arm. I turned away, left Lacey gazing at the bare-torsoed boys and girls.

The band was about to move off at the head of the Parade. The opening notes of 'O'Donnell Abu' blasted out, the band lurched off across Madam's Bridge and onto the Main Street, followed by a cohort of Indians, horses rearing, plunging, pintos, palominos, one grey, skittering sideways, crowding onto the heels of the band, riders screaming war cries.

Hooves clattered, Indians yelled, the band played, people applauded, cheered, called out.

Men clutching pints stepped from the seductive gloom of pubs, sleeves of their white shirts turned up onto tanned forearms, squinting in the glare as they viewed the passing parade.

'Would ya like some firewater, Evie?' a pint-clutcher shouted.

'Don't bloody well mind if I do,' she answered.

In the confusion at the gateway Judo and I managed to sneak

into the field without paying. Inside was a multicoloured array of amusements: swinging boats, big ones for adults, small ones for children. And Chairoplanes, already full and flying round and round. There was a Rifle Range, Wheel of Fortune, Roulette Wheel, Pongo and Roll-A-Penny.

'In the square/ the money is fair/ on the line/ the money is mine,' a man called out, over and over, as people laid coins on numbers and watched the penny come rolling down the groove, willing it to land full-square on their number. It rarely landed squarely on any number.

High overhead, fixed to the red truss that carried the swinging boats, a double, trumpet shaped loudspeaker blared music across the roofs of the town. It eddied off, growing fainter and fainter, fading away into silence in the blueness above the surrounding hills.

'You walk like an angel, talk like an angel, but I got wise...' Elvis was singing over the heads of pram-pushing mothers, children, dogs, white-shirted men, all mingling ceaselessly, moving from one attraction to another.

Out on the playing field stewards rushed urgently about trying to organise the parade into orderly formations for the judges as the band pounded out 'The Wearing of the Green.'

Country people that I'd rarely seen in town and town people who hardly ever moved away from their houses strolled about in their good clothes, drawn out of their routine by the colour and excitement of the Carnival. Even the blind woman from Barrack Street was strolling about, clutching the arm of her neighbour, Mrs. O'Riordan. I watched a man with one short leg go by, jerking along wearing one boot with a thickened sole. And Simon Cantwell, in his ragged top coat, making no concessions to Sunday.

'C'mon,' said Judo, dragging on my arm.

Mary Black Pudding, swarthy and exotic, dressed in baggy black trousers and silver-studded waistcoat was performing a sideshow in a grassy space close to the towering town wall. He cycled from town to town, performing his stunts wherever crowds gathered. He swung a long whip theatrically, made it crack with a sound like a rifleshot to attract attention. He lay alternately on a bed of nails or on broken glass with a huge rock resting on his chest. Sometimes he'd invite someone to stand on his chest. There were tiny shards of glass stuck to his bare back when he stood up. And flecks of blood.

'C'mon,' said Judo.

We ran to the bumpers – Dodgems a sign proclaimed – battered, smelly veterans of many long years doing the rounds of summer carnivals in small towns. Showers of white sparks streamed and fell like a million dying stars as tall rods on the back of the bumpers jigged along the mesh overhead. Red, green, yellow, blue, the cars roared and spun through a confetti of fading sparks. An overpowering stench of scorching rubber filled the air all around. Occasionally, inexplicably, the power would suddenly die, the cars stop abruptly, then lurch off again to delighted screams.

It was the busiest part of the Carnival with a constant crush at the steps as people jostled impatiently, waiting for cars to be vacated.

At last we got a car then screamed hysterically, Judo at the wheel, as we spun and zig zagged around the arena, sometimes keeping to the outside, sometimes ploughing recklessly into the centre.

Judo was intent on chasing Spud Murphy, a mechanic who sped along The Valley every evening on his Honda 175. He was piloting a red bumper car. Round and round he sped, keeping to the outside, a black, white-banded hat slanted over his eyes, cigarette in the corner of his mouth, nonchalantly avoiding anyone who tried to bump him with an effortless, one-handed twirl of the steering wheel.

Finally, just as the session ended Judo rammed him full on from behind driving him into the rear of another car. He jerked forward, lost the cigarette from his mouth and hat from his head.

'You walk like an angel...,' Judo roared, then ran for it as Spud lunged towards him across the bumper.

163

They disappeared into the crowd.

I wandered over to the Pongo tent. Filled mostly with women. The mother was seated there, gently rocking baby Tom in his pram, Gerry and Frank waiting to mark off the numbers on the hand-painted board with bottle tops. I slipped quickly away before they realised I was there and started bawling to come with me.

Spud Murphy was now at the Rifle Range carefully patting darts with fluffy pink flights into a rifle.

'Tell that wizened little shitehawk I'll brain him the next time we meet, and you're lucky I don't kick the bejasus outa you too,' he said, when he saw me.

'I did nothing on you,' I said.

Then watched and rejoiced as he fired his five darts to the left of the target.

'Hey, this yoke is shooting to the left,' he said, to the man in charge.

'Adjust your aim so,' the man grunted.

'How about giving me me money back?' Spud demanded.

The man answered with a withering look.

I moved quickly away.

Sporadic cheers sounded from the playing field as different categories of parade winners were announced. Tractors and lorries began inching slowly through the crowd and out the main gate. Two girls in fairy costumes wandered around eating candyfloss off a stick. A boy on a donkey wearing jockey's silks moved through the crowd. Drumming his heels on the donkey's ribs to keep him in motion.

As soon as the playing field was cleared a shortened pitch was set up for a seven-a-side football tournament.

Suddenly Judo appeared from between the Pongo and the Wheel of Fortune stalls.

'He's still looking for you,' I said, nodding towards the Rifle Range.

'All right, he'll be going home to milk the cows soon – I seen his aul' fella below in the Bridge guzzling large bottles,' Judo said, 'c'mon we'll go up on the swinging boats.'

'Don't be windy now, no hanging on to the bar, pull with yer two hands,' he said, as the attendant set us in motion.

The swinging boat creaked, rocked, its rigid bars rattled, we pulled hard, and harder, higher and higher. We soared above everything, dropped suddenly down in a rush, then up, up, skyward once more. Judo later claimed that he'd seen clear over the red truss on which the boats swung, had seen Jimmy Grey's hair net fly off after a hefty tackle out on the field in the seven a side game.

Judo and I pulled and pulled, stood in the boat, reaching higher along the rope, leaning back, striving to drive it higher than anybody had ever driven one before, but we were all of us swinging in the same pre-determined arc.

As the afternoon edged on towards evening a steady stream of people began drifting away from the attractions and out through the main gate: country people going to their bikes, ponies and traps, asses and carts, cars – whatever had brought them to town for the day. Peter Hegarty came rattling up from The Pound where his ass and cart had been tethered all afternoon. A widow woman in black wheeled her bike from behind the safe haven of the chapel gates.

All leaving the blare of the Carnival, going home along the narrow roads and laneways that wound through the quiet fields of the countryside.

Townspeople walked slowly back to their houses, paused, chatted, prolonged things, savoured the happenings of a day that was out of the ordinary. Most moved with a satisfied air of completeness, their day out coming to a slow, pleasurable end.

Others headed for the railway station to get the mystery train.

Some carried cheap prizes won at the Wheel of Fortune or the Rifle Range: a man went by carrying an outsized teddy bear. A woman passed with a ceramic shepherdess lying at her child's feet in the pram.

Judo and I had moved down to The Square, were sitting on the vantage point known as The Chair, two huge limestone blocks bum-polished by generations of men with little to do but sit for hours talking and looking at a mostly empty street. Where even a dog passing was an event to be noted.

We sat there feeding long strings of blackjack into our mouths. Brother Virgilius passed, out for an evening stroll, to aid his digestion most likely, dogless still, looking slightly bereft.

He nodded curtly.

'*Dia is Mhuire dhib,*' he said.

It sounded like a threat.

We mumbled a reply.

The sergeant came along in his black boots, baton in its round case at his side. He'd been ready for riots all right. The green door of the barracks clicked shut behind his ball alley back.

'Roses are red, my love, violets are blue...' Ronnie Carroll was singing through the loudspeaker now, the sound muffled by the thickness of the town wall at our backs.

The brass band roared by, heading for home in an ancient, lopsided bus billowing plumes of black smoke.

The mother and Mamie came along, moving lazily towards The Valley. Pausing now and then as Mamie made a point. The mother in a light blue summer dress closely patterned with white flowerlets. Varicose veins showing on her thin legs.

'Well, what did ye make of Evie and her Indians?' Mamie asked, stopping in front of us, 'did ye ever see the like of her in them buckskins, and the bucking horses, you wouldn't be sure o' your life, ye should never trust a horse's hind leg.'

Mary Black Pudding freewheeled by on his big bike, his bed of nails and broken glass in tow on a little home-made trailer. The black whip coiled around his shoulders and across his chest like a Mexican bandolero.

The bullet-headed boys came racing round the corner from the field, at full tilt, rushing to make the train at six o'clock.

The mother made us a salad for supper. Hardboiled eggs, scallions, lettuce, tomatoes, never tasted so fresh. Judo called and we ran back towards the Barrack Field along an empty, yawning Main Street. It was always empty, always yawning, but seemed achingly so after the colour and hubbub of the parade. We paused

166

for a moment to watch Tommy Kerwick, the melodeon player, step unsteadily from Scully's bar, a tumbleweed of blue smoke rolling after him through the door. He leaned delicately forward, placing one shoulder against a light pole. Beer poured from his open mouth as water would from a tilted barrel, splashed onto the street. He wiped his mouth, pulled on his fag, went back inside. It seemed as though he had come out to empty himself. Within seconds the sound of his melodeon came to our ears. Being played at manic speed.

I opened the door. We peeped into the smoky interior of the pub.

Men were screeching, pouring Guinness from large bottles into frothy glasses, clapping, shouting, good on ya, Tommy, boy, good on ya; a fat, bald man spun round and round, red-faced, with a thin woman, both paddling madly with their outside leg, spinning faster, faster, laughing, laughing, madly, under a bank of blue cigarette smoke. Suddenly everyone stopped, roared 'Fine girl y'are,' then launched into the chorus as Tommy jigged and sidestepped, opening and closing the accordion like a madman. A madman surrounded by men and women momentarily mad, for whom morning had become a distant mirage that might never materialise.

We ran on to the Barrack Field only to find that all was quiet, anti-climactic, flattened grass littered with the day's debris. Dogs sniffing at chip bags. Ned Miller singing overhead 'And Lady Luck played her hand just right ...' the swell and the beat of the music echoing desolately off the old town walls.

A tournament hurling game between Killenaule and Ballingarry dragged along with just a scatter of spectators. The usual tension absent. We hung around the bumpers, no money in our pockets, enviously watching the few cars coursing round, mostly fellows with their squealing girlfriends who'd forsaken the flicks and the double seats this Sunday evening for the Carnival attractions.

We hung around until darkness began to gather round the edge of things, came stealing across the silent football field. Was held back by the halo of yellowish light that encircled the amusements.

167

One by one the couples walked away into the twilight, probably heading for some corner of the Back Lane or Jesuits' Walk.

In the end, reluctantly, we gave up. The day had fizzled out. We made our way home along the Main Street, a half-lit, gloomy underworld of shifting shadows now that daylight had been replaced by sparse street lighting and a yellowish glow from windows and doorways. We kept close together, Judo and I, were anxious to get home, get off that now unfamiliar street, with its shadows and dark places that could conceal God knew what.

I recognised the familiar, hated shape of John Lacey propped against the jamb of Scully's door.

'C'mere to me, c'mere me aul' segotia, have ya e'er a fag?' he called.

We ran to the far side of the street.

Then sprinted for home.

Later I lay in bed, listening to Paudie breathing deeply, lost to the world in dreams. Juggling a dozen different images of the day, elusive as quicksilver as sleep slowly took hold.

# 33

# Breaking The Pledge

Next day it was all gone. A world dismantled as we slept. Being set up anew in another town even as we became aware of its absence. Leaving only a dull, irritating ache as the weight of the ordinary came down on us once more. Carnivals and circuses always arrived and left like that - coming and going, brief as a dream before waking.

I woke up one morning and out of nowhere the amusements had arrived – then in no time at all I was waking to find they had gone. Disappearing along country roads, only barking dogs and curious cattle to see them pass.

We went up to the Barrack Field, first thing. All of us, the entire gang. Hoping to find something, anything. Mostly though we were hoping to find some coins. Maybe some had slipped from the roulette table, or from someone's pocket on the bumpers. Slid down through the cracks and into the whitened grass below. Finding a shilling, a tanner, even a threepenny bit, would have been as precious to us as a gold-strike to an old prospector. But all that greeted us was an empty space that stared eerily, and obscene-looking patches of dead, whitened grass where the sideshows and attractions had stood for those few precious days. There would be no more rushing to get here in the evenings after supper.

And we found no coins.

The Patrick's Place gang had probably been there well before us.

We trudged back to the camp, disheartened. Restless, adjusting to the loss, casting about in our minds, trying to think of something that would erase thoughts of the departed carnival.

After a while Judo and I split from the rest of the gang, left them languishing morosely around the camp. Snapping at one another.

We just mooched off, not headed anywhere in particular, streeling slowly from sleeper to tarry sleeper along the railway line until we came to the railway station. It was deserted. Nothing stirred. The dog stretched on the platform didn't even get up as we passed, just lifted his head a little, wagged his tail half-heartedly from where he lay.

We peeped through the window of the empty signal box. We passed under the high, arched opening where trains entered the goods store. A number of boxes and tea chests were stacked on the platform.

Paddy the Racket was backing his off-white old nag and cart into the loading bay.

'Back away, set, back away, set,' he was saying, softly, over and over, as the old horse pushed his hindquarters against the britchen.

'Howya Paddy?' Judo said.

'Feck off with yeerselves now, go on, feck off,' Paddy answered.

He began loading his cart.

We watched his hunched figure shuffling back and forth pushing a handcart, asked him which shops the boxes were for and what was in them.

He simply blasted his bony nose clear with one finger, spat onto the platform and ignored us.

Nothing could break his morose concentration as he devoted himself totally to the job of stacking the boxes on the cart.

Eventually he sat onto the cart, shook the reins, spoke to the horse and left the station with a thunderous rattle of iron-hooped wheels.

'Shaggin aul' piss-arse,' said Judo, watching him go.

We listened to the noise of the wheels on the road, like the thunder of a distant battle.

When Paddy was gone we amused ourselves walking along the walls of the pens that were used on fair day Tuesdays to hold cattle waiting to be loaded onto cattle wagons. Our balancing act ended when Tom Ryan, the stationmaster, appeared on the platform and shouted at us to clear off. We ran onto the Cashel road and walked the short distance back to town.

Tom Hanley was watering his cows in the river under the convent bridge. Just finished milking.

He had a cowhouse and haybarn behind his house even though it was in the town. His cows were slow-moving creatures with big bellies, bulging bones and swinging udders. They scuttered constantly after their day grazing: on the street, on footpaths, spattering onto newly-painted walls, the cows were very democratic, didn't mind where they did it – everybody and everything was included.

We hopped, skipped and jumped across trails of freshly-dropped cows' scutter on the road outside Tom's house. Peggie, Tom's wife was in the doorway, swaying slightly on spindly legs and high heels.

'C'mere to me, let ye,' she said, beckoning.

We stepped into the hallway. A picture of a man in a suit and hat hung on the wall facing the door.

'Who's that fella?' I asked.

'*That* fella is me father, he fought and died for Ireland, so he did,' Peggie said, with pride.

'Where was he shot?' Judo asked.

'Above in the GPO, gunned down with Pearse,' said Peggie.

'Pearse wasn't shot in the GPO, was he?' Judo asked, cautiously.

'Never mind all that aul' history now, I want ye to do a jobeen for me,' she said.

I could smell the porter on her breath.

She handed Judo a message bag. A dull, glassy clink sounded. She pressed two half-crowns into my hand.

'Go down to the Bridge Bar, let ye, and get me three large Guinness, and a Baby Power, quick now, and don't drop that message bag on the way back no matter what happens,' she said.

On the way back Judo opened the bag, lifted a bottle and hid it behind the low wall in front of the cinema.

171

'Jaysus, Judo, what are ya doing, we'll be in right trouble when she misses that – and what are ya going to do with it anyway?' I said.

'We'll sample it, or better still, sell it to Mickey Harney, he drinks large bottles,' Judo said.

My mind flashed back to the episode with Fritz and Virgilius. We'd been meant to get money out of that too.

Peggie was bound to report us to the sergeant, he was bound to call to see the father – *I* was bound to get a trimming.

'I dunno, Judo, I dunno,' I said.

Our day had started badly, now it was about to get an awful lot worse.

My guilt intensified when Peggie gave us tuppence each and Judo just had to go overboard thanking her, telling what a grand dacent woman she was compared to some of the aul' skinflints we did jobs for who wouldn't give you the steam off their you-know-what, beggin' your pardon Peggie.

I thought we'd never get out of that house.

Peggie had placed the message bag on the kitchen table, was poised to open it.

'Sure poor aul' Tom is fond of his bottleen and a Woodbine after the evening milking, I do have an odd drop o' the craythur meself, strictly on doctor's orders, as a class of a tonic, just to build meself up like,' Peggie said, flashing us a terrifying, one-toothed, smile.

I knew there wouldn't be as much as a dreeder left in those bottles by the time evening milking came round.

I gave Judo a determined kick on the ankle. We flashed out that door like swallows from a cow house, collected Judo's hidden bottle and flew.

At Ned Meagher's we bought a few lengths of liquorice and some broken biscuits, then set off along the riverbank. At Coffey's mill we stopped to eat the liquorice.

The water level in the river was low and one of the eyes in the bridge was dry except for a shallow sheet of water. We went in there and sat out of sight on a couple of big rocks covered in half-dried moss. It was gloomy and the smell of the drying riverbed was heavy. Judo levered at the cap with his flick knife until it loosened and brown froth fizzed out. Eventually it flew off.

Judo raised it to his mouth.

'Strictly on doctor's orders,' he said, and took a swig.

'Ah,' he said grimacing, 'tis as bitter as bejasus.'

He drank again, then passed it to me.

'I'll be breaking my pledge,' I said.

'Feck the pledge,' Judo said.

'All right so, but only for the good o' me health,' I said

'A tonic,' says Judo.

'To build meself up like,' I said.

The smell was sour, the taste bitter, I tried to swallow and it fizzed down my nose.

'Go again, go again,' Judo said, 'tisn't as bitter on the second slug.'

I took a bigger, bolder swig and felt it trickle slowly down, spreading like warm lava into my stomach.

Judo produced a topped fag and lit up.

'Flow gently, Sweet Afton,' he said, inhaling deeply, then coughed until tears ran from his eyes.

Back and forth we passed the bottle, sharing every second drag on the Sweet Afton. We kept going until the large bottle was empty and the fag-end sizzling in the water.

'We better bring Peggie back her empty, she'll want it tomorrow,' Judo said.

'Get me fifteen large Guinness, like good little boys,' I said, and began laughing madly.

Everything seemed bright, really bright. Strange light-shapes reflected from the shallow strip of water moved mysteriously on the arch overhead. I began to feel wildly happy with the world: the sergeant, Virgilius, Horse, all seemed to be the most wonderful people on earth. I felt a sudden urge to do something, felt that nothing was impossible.Suddenly Judo jumped to his feet, banging his head on the arch of the bridge.

'Well, Jaysus,' he roared.

Then suddenly started to sing.

'When I get tired and feeling blue,

I think of all the things that we do,

In summer,'

'Summer,' I sang, echoing the refrain.

'Yahoo…' Judo roared, 'Daveee, Daveeee Crockett, King of the wild frontier.'

'Born on a mountain-top in Tennessee…' I sang.

'Daveee, Daveee Crockett…' Judo interrupted.

He took off then like a scalded cat, splashing through the water, out onto the bank of the river, me after him, laughing hysterically. A cow and her two calves took flight around the field, the two of us chasing them, running madly through buttercups, daisies and tall thistles. Judo managed to grab a calf's tail and held it for one split second before losing his grip and tumbling into a clump of buachalainns.

I landed beside him. We lay there, laughing sporadically, trying to get our breath back.

When I stood up the bridge and the field heaved suddenly skyward.

'Look, Judo, I'm on a see-saw,' I shouted.

And fell over.

I got to my hands and knees, and tumbled over again.

'Hey Judo, there's something wrong with me legs, I can't shaggin well stand,' I shouted.

'I can't either,' Judo said.

I looked up at the sky. It seemed a long, long way above me.

'Jonno, Jonno, me aul' segotia,' Judo said, crawling over to me, putting an arm around my shoulders.

We made our way onto the bridge and leaned over the parapet. I stared at the foaming water rushing below. Stared long and hard until it seemed I was standing on the stern of a boat and the water below was rushing backwards in our wake and the land on either side was flowing past. I began to feel dizzy. The bridge seemed to spin.

'Ah, Judo, Jaysus, Judo I'm gonta…' I said.

174

'Whassup with ye boys?' a voice asked from behind.

It was John Lacey. Complete with bike, fork and slasher angled up along the crossbar.

'Will ya do a message for me later on?' he asked me.

I pointed at Judo.

'He...' I started to say and got violently sick onto Lacey's wellingtons.

'Ya little feckin' reptile,' he shouted, 'wait'll I tell yer aul' wan what ya did, you'll be in trouble then, I can smell the porter offa ye, oh, wait'll I tell her, you'll know all about it then, so ya will.'

'Sure you can wash the wellingtons in the shallow part of the river, or above at the Judy,' Judo said, helpfully.

'Maybe I'll have something to tell her, too,' I spluttered, spitting and hawking, full of false courage.

I felt a second wave coming on.

'What d'ya mane, I don't care what ya tell her, so I don't,' he answered.

He swung onto his bike and pedalled away, muttering and cursing.

Judo looked at me.

'What did ya mean there with yer "maybe I'll have something to tell her, too"?' he asked.

'I want to lie down Judo, ohhhhhh, Jaysus, Judo, Jaysus, just let me lie down for a while,' I said.

We walked unsteadily into the field, lay down and fell asleep. When I lifted my aching head again the cow and her two calves were gazing at us, ears angled forward quizzically. The Abbey bell was tolling out the Angelus. The day was gone, lost to the large bottle and sleep. My mouth felt as though I'd been eating dust.

I began to feel something like respect, even awe, for Peggie. I had often wondered why she tottered a little as she walked across the bridge every day with her message bag. Now I knew. Twice a day she made that trip, morning and afternoon. That was six large bottles of Guinness and two Baby Powers.

How could she even stand after all that? On those spindly legs?

And here were we stretched out after one bottle between us.

175

I pictured her sitting there in the kitchen supping away bottle after bottle all day long. Sometimes you'd see the curtain on the kitchen window move a little as you passed.

I kicked Judo on the hip.

'C'mon willya,' I said.

For once Judo had absolutely nothing to say. Except for sighs and groans he was silent.

We made our way to the Judy at the lower end of The Valley and drank a lot of water.

Then made our way home in silence to our supper.

Next day Peggie appeared suddenly at the door as Judo and I were passing on our way to the camp.

'C'mere to me, c'mere to me, ye feckin highwaymen, where's me bottle, ye owe me a large bottle, poor Tom missed his fill o' porter on account o' ye, I'll have the sergeant on to ye all right, if ye don't bring back me bottle,' she said.

'We'll have it back tomorrow, Peggie,' Judo said.

That evening we left the empty bottle on her doorstep.

'Now Peggie, there's your aul' bottle back,' Judo said.

'I'd say she meant us to leave back a full one,' I said.

'Full one me arse,' said Judo, as we turned away and ran.

We didn't hear anymore from Peggie about the large bottle. Once or twice she rapped at the window as we passed, making us take off as if we'd heard a starting pistol.

The episode with the bottle had lasted only a few hours: but I suffered for it with weeks of fearful guilt as I slunk around terrified of meeting the sergeant, turning in the opposite direction whenever I saw him approach. Anytime he passed along The Valley I was on edge until he'd gone past our door. A long time went by before I felt we were out of trouble and could forget about Peggie and how I'd broken my pledge with one of her large bottles.

# 34

# Leaving

Spikey came strolling out of Kerry Street carrying a small suitcase. The usual fag dangling from the corner of his mouth.

A right looking spiv, Mamie would say, whenever she saw him with the fag like that.

He turned onto the Cashel road, heading for the railway station to catch the nine o'clock train that would arrive from Dublin and get him to Rosslare in time for the night sailing. Next morning he'd be a world away, stepping out onto the platform of Paddington station in London. Judo and I slid off the polished parapet of the bridge and ran after him.

'All right?' he said, when we caught him up.

Not saying much we walked with him up the wide gravel driveway that led to the cut-stone building of the railway station. I'd often seen people make the long, slow walk from the town to the railway station to catch that evening train. I'd seen young fellows, aged sixteen sometimes seventeen, make the walk for the first time. Heading for London, usually. Mostly though, I'd seen married men make the slow walk up to the station heading back to England after the Christmas or the summer break. Leaving their families behind.

Once I'd seen Paddy Lawrence walking past a toss school on Sunday evening. The men in their suits and dusty shoes had continued with their game. One or two calling out a 'good luck,' or 'see ya' to Paddy. Without a pause in their gambling. Men coming and going from London wasn't something that would give anyone reason to pause.

Judo and I stood with Spikey on the platform, awaiting the train. Spikey smoking, us not saying much.

During the two weeks that he'd been around I'd never really got a chance to talk to Spikey. I'd had to admire him from afar.

His prowess with girls had stirred deep envy in the Horse.

I was disappointed in him. He wasn't really all that different from the other fellas who were in London when you took away the fancy clobber, which was what he called clothes. He dressed differently but did more or less the same things as they did.

Except he went in for the ladies, they went in for the lump.

The train whistle sounded in the distance.

'Be a bloody relief to get away from this kip,' he said.

'Might see ye for the Christmas so mates,' he said, as he got into the train.

'He's probably going away to get a rest from all those girls,' Judo said.

I never saw Spikey again. Nobody ever knew what became of him.

# 35

# Youghal By The Sea

We were all sitting in the kitchen. Waiting. Whispering, nudging one another occasionally. Paudie's day had come. He was all dressed up, ready to go. Wearing a tie and long trousers. The tie he'd worn for his confirmation only last year. The mother had got the trousers somewhere. We suspected it had belonged to one of the bank manager's sons who lived down the road in a house set among trees and immaculate flowerbeds. The boys were a bit older than Paudie and kept well away from us. Mr. Hartigan, the bank manager, had a car and sometimes you'd see them driving off on sunny Sundays. We always suspected they were going to Tramore and thought badly of them because of that. None of us had ever been to Tramore. Paudie and Horse had been there once but that was a Legion of Mary outing which didn't really count because of all the Rosaries and litanies they had to say going there and coming back.

The mother had spent an hour with needle and thread turning up the legs of the trousers. Paudie didn't want to wear it but had to give in because he didn't want to go away looking like a schoolboy in short trousers.

'I'm not wearing anyone's cast-offs,' he'd said.

He meant cast-offs from anyone who lived on our road and looked down on us.

Kept aloof from us. Laughed at us.

If it had come in a parcel from England he wouldn't have minded.

'What are we waiting for Mam?' Gerry asked.

'Your brother Paudie is waiting on his lift, I told you,' the mother said.

'Is that why he's all dressed up in Thomas Hartigan's britches?' Gerry asked.

'Shut *up* willya,' Paudie snapped.

'They're not Thomas Hartigan's trousers, who told you they were Thomas Hartigan's trousers?' the mother asked.

'Jonno did,' Gerry said.

'I did not,' I shouted, lying.

'You did so ya did,' Gerry said.

'The cheek of you, there's nothing at all wrong with them trousers,' the mother said, eyeing me.

She turned to Paudie.

'He should be here any minute now,' she said.

Paudie didn't answer. I'd never seen him so quiet.

None of us had anything to say.

Silence set in.

Horse's hooves and the rattle of draught chains could be heard. Faint at first, growing louder as they passed, fading again in the direction of the creamery.

Mick Hogan, a cattle dealer, was to call for Paudie at half-nine. He was delivering calves to a farmer somewhere near Youghal and was going to drop Paudie off at the hotel. He'd played football with the father and would be glad to do him this favour.

At ten o'clock the squeal of brakes sounded outside.

'That's him,' the mother said.

There was noise again: chairs scraping on the concrete floor, a subdued babble of voices. The awful shudder of the engine outside.

Paudie picked up the old message bag in which he'd packed a few items of clothing. The rest of us rushed out to see Mick Hogan's dilapidated old calf truck.

It listed slightly at the passenger side and stank of animal piss. Calves pressed snuffling noses to the slatted sides of the truck. Others bawled mournfully. Leaving their familiar fields behind.

'Have you everything now?' the mother asked Paudie.

'Yeah,' he answered, sharply, keeping his eyes on the ground.

The mother sprinkled him with holy water.

'For fecks' sake, Mam,' he said.

'Willya write me a letter?' I asked.

I'd never gotten a letter in the post.

'Feck off,' Paudie said.

He climbed into the cab, kept looking straight ahead. It seemed to me that he was on the verge of tears.

'Don't worry now, Missus,' Mick Hogan said, 'I'll get him there all in one piece, it might be a bit late in the evening, but sure what matter, I'll give a shout on the way back, good luck to ye all now.'

He revved the engine, the truck roared in distress as it moved off and laboured down the road, black smoke billowing from beneath the trailer.

Suddenly it seemed to me that Youghal was the most distant and lonesomest place imaginable, that the journey there was going to be so long and so slow for Paudie who'd only ever been as far as Tramore for a few hours and was now heading off on his own to a strange place.

The mother hardly spoke a word all through that day. She made us all kneel in the kitchen at bedtime to say the Rosary for Paudie.

It was late, after ten, when Mick Hogan called. He came in for a cup of tea out of his hand, smelling of whiskey.

'A grand quiet young fella, a credit to ye, he'll do well for himself all right,' he said.

The mother had a whole lot of questions, she wanted to know what the hotel looked like, what kind of a man the manager was.

'Grand, grand,' Mick answered to all her questions.

Everything was grand.

That night I missed Paudie from beside me in the bed. I missed the whispered chats we used to have. Even if, more often than not, he would shunt me to the edge of the bed with his backside, tell me to go to sleep and not be pestering him with my stupid questions.

For a long time afterwards the mother was quiet in herself. The father would give out to her. That young fella'll be grand, grand, sure there's no need for you to be worrying, he'd say.

We didn't talk about Paudie much, but we thought about him and missed him from the house and from the camp as well.

Missed him a lot.

# 36

# Battle Of The Abbey Rocks

Afterwards, during those early winter days when Christmas seems an eternity away and summer a fading memory, we always spoke of it as a battle. Dramatised it. Capitalised it: THE BATTLE OF THE ABBEY ROCKS. Like the big blood-red print you'd sometimes see flashing across the screen in a trailer at the Capitol cinema. As if it had been an epic clash.

In truth, though, it had been a mere skirmish one Thursday evening late in July that briefly lifted the summer ennui that was settling on us.

But at the time, and for a long time after, whenever we sat in the camp and talked of our encounter with the estate gang there was always a euphoric feeling about the whole thing. A desire to elevate it to the realm of the heroic, glory in imagined deeds of valour. Swash and buckle a bit, like Errol Flynn, across the big screen of the imagination. Align ourselves with great fictional heroes. Which was fitting enough, since our heroics were fictional too. Our noble memories were really just a self-serving deception.

Pony, I mean *Pony*, who would run like a rabbit from his own shadow, boasted stupidly of how he had taken on Big Joe Ryan, when everyone knew he'd made sure to get himself well away from Big Joe. Had, in fact, run away at the end.

It was always like that when we told of things afterwards: fellas exaggerating, embellishing, magnifying their own part in events and happenings. Minimising what others had done.

Like that aul' fecker of a John Lacey shouldering us aside in games of street football, trying to make out he was a hero fit to wear the blue and gold when half the time he was shuffling around like Barney Wattletoes.

And that's how it was with us after the Abbey Rocks and our

encounter with the Patrick's Place gang – even though we'd come out on the worst side of it.

There had always been an edgy rivalry between our gang and all of the other gangs in the town. Each street had its own gang, its own identity. And gangs mostly stuck to their own territory.

Sometimes we promoted and exaggerated our difference from the other gangs.

When really we weren't all that different.

Sitting around our campfire, great rushes of pride and a kind of patriotic fervour would flare through us when talking of how much better we were than any of the others and how we'd sacrifice ourselves for the sake of the gang.

The Valley Gang, that's what we were, The Valley Gang. Miles ahead of, and superior to, all the other gangs in the town. Main Street, Burke Street, The Green, Patrick's Place, it didn't matter, we told ourselves we were better than all of them. And different. We could make bows and arrows, catapults, better than any of the other gangs. Fight better than them, run faster and farther than them, climb trees better than them, rob orchards better than them. Our camp was better than any other camp. Our teepees were almost like real Indian teepees. We were the Indians battling the white eyes, proud, noble, unwilling to take flight or surrender in a fight no matter what. They could pin us to the ground all day – we would never cry or give up.

Only a week or so before the Abbey Rocks incident a few of us had run into Buckledup, Big Joe's younger brother. Strangely, he was wading alone in the river down from the stile in front of our house. We'd watched him for a while, a wolfpack about to descend on its prey. A two pound jampot in his hand, completely absorbed in trying to catch brickileens.

He'd jumped when Judo had challenged him.

'Hey, Buckledup, Buckledup, bockety legs, knobbly knees, whaddya think you're doing down here, trespassing on our territory, eh?' Judo said.

Buckledup had straightened, water and brickileens streaming from his jamjar.

'Jaysus lads, I'm only looking for a few aul' rout ags,' he said.

'Rout ags me hole,' Pony had roared.

We'd blindfolded him, staked him to the ground, spreadeagled, just as we'd seen Indians do it in films. Threatened to sting him with nettles. Then left him there for a while bawling, before cutting the binding twine from his wrists. He was relieved. Until Judo and Pony caught him and threw him into the river.

'I'll be telling our Joe on ye, he'll bate the shite outa ye, so he will, our Joe is the toughest fella in Fethard, ye'll be sorry, I'm telling ye now,' he bawled as he squelched and dripped his way back to the road, his two wellingtons full of water.

'Maybe the rout ags are in yer wellingtons,' Judo shouted after him.

'We don't care who ya tell, we're The Valley Gang,' Pony shouted.

'WE DON'T GIVE A HANG,

WE'RE THE VALLEY GANG,'

we chanted, elated with a feeling of power and a sense of being indestructible as a gang.

We knew, though, that there was a possibility of repercussions. Staking the gang leader's younger brother to the ground hadn't been very clever. But by then we were without Paudie, who was in Youghal. And Horse was not with us.

I don't even know what brought us to the Rocks on that Thursday evening. Mostly we only went there on Sunday afternoons to re-enact whatever film we'd seen in the matinee at the Capitol. Especially if it was a Western. Although we did re-enact gangster films, Roman films, war films – anything that was full of action.

But we ended up in the Rocks, drifting aimlessly over humps and into hollows, through clumps of fading, yellow-topped buachalainns, skirting round patches of buck nettles that still had a vicious sting; popping lazily over toothy briars; following dusty cattle tracks made by the friars' cows that twisted, looped and merged one into the other, not seeming to lead anywhere. We wandered along, with vacant enough minds, vaguely hoping to come upon some distraction that would relieve the ennui of a long Thursday afternoon with *The Beano* and *The Dandy* already read. Of course we would read them again later but that would be going over old ground. We needed something there and then, to fill out those empty moments. So we wandered on not expecting much, drawn on by the illusion that the clumps of bushes and ochre-stained juttings of limestone concealed some secret, some surprise that would stir our tired imaginations.

Well, there *was* a surprise lying in wait for us. It hit when the circuitous cattle track led us to the river where the cows went for water. We turned right to walk along its banks. There was high ground rising steeply away to our right. Rocky, bushy uneven ground. The kind of ground that you'd always see ambushes launched from in Westerns.

And that's where they came from, the Patrick's Place gang. Whooping and screeching down the hill towards us. We paused.

'Ruuuuuun,' Judo roared.

And we ran.

Instinctively seeking some spot where we could make our stand. Somewhere with cover at our backs. It had to be the bridge. Old, decrepit, creaking, the wooden bridge that spanned the river had been built with old railway sleepers to bring the cows from the Rocks to the cow house behind the Abbey at milking time. The meadow was surrounded by stone walls that looked as dateless as the old Abbey. The gate at the other end of the field led to the cow house.

'Jaysus, we're going to be kilt,' Judo shouted.

'Stop, stop here, we'll make our stand on the bridge,' Pony roared.

We stopped, milled around in desperation and were immediately overrun by sheer force of numbers. I was knocked over, groped around in the layers of dried and fresh cow dung that covered the railway sleepers.

'Die, Valley bastard,' Pug Moroney roared.

His big meaty knee met me on in the temple and that ended the Battle of the Abbey Rocks for me. I managed to stand, briefly, the ground heaved and swayed under me, then rose abruptly like the end of a see-saw that someone had jumped off. I hit the sleepers once more. Unconscious.

When I came round there was a circle of faces looking down at me. Curious more than concerned, wanting to see how I was affected.

'He's not dead anyway,' a voice said.

That was Joe Ryan.

'Jaysus he've a wicked knob on his forrid.'

That was Judo.

'Here, give him some water,' said Philly Landy, kneeling beside me with an old Walpamur paint tin full of water.

He tipped some filthy, cow-shitty water onto my face.

'For feck's sake, Philly,' I said, rolling onto my side.

The ground heaved again and I puked.

'Ah for fuck's sake me good gutties,' Philly roared.

'We thought you were feckin well dead,' Judo said.

'Well if this is heaven yeer some feckin angels,' I said.

'Put a cowld stone again that knob,' Joe Ryan said, helpfully.

Judo got one from the river.

'I'll be kilt if I go home with a knob on me forrid,' I said.

'An' all that cowshit on yer clothes,' Philly pointed out, helpfully.

Gradually the knob shrunk and the dizziness went away.

It seemed that all of the gang except for Judo, Philly and me, had continued running across the bridge instead of making a stand.

'We stood back to back, like the Three Musketeers,' Philly said, proudly.

I didn't remember standing back to back with anybody. Only landing on my back when I was struck down by a meaty knee. Some hero.

'Yahoo, all for one and one for all,' Philly shouted.

I sat up, then stood. Gradually the dizziness left me.

The Patrick's Place gang lifted the three of us shoulder high and carried us from the river bank back to the road, saying we were the bravest of the brave to stand and face their gang on the bridge.

'Hopelessly outnumbered,' said Big Joe, 'battling against overwhelming odds.'

'The 300 Spartans,' Judo roared, 'that's what we're like, the fucken 300 Spartans.'

'And me like brave Horatius, the captain of the gate,' I shouted, suddenly remembering the ancient Roman hero that we'd learned about in a poem at school.

He'd held a bridge against a whole army of invaders. Only trouble was, he'd been killed, like all three hundred of the Spartans. None of us dwelt on that though, we only saw the heroics.

'That was some fight all right,' Judo said, when the Patrick's Place lads were gone.

Judo seemed more confident and commanding now that Pony had shown weakness in running away.

'Ye stood on either hand and kept the bridge with me,' I said, throwing an inclusive arm around their shoulders as we made our way back to The Valley and home.

Puffed up with the notion that we were some kind of heroes, the myth that we would create and brag about already forming in our minds.

# 37

# The Canon's Garden

'I know,' said Jim, 'we'll raid the Rectory orchard.'

Everyone perked up immediately.

The Rectory. Home of the Protestant minister, Canon Haythornthwaite. With a posh accent like all the gentry who lived on estates in the hinterland of the old town.

Coming to town in their Hillmans and Cambridges, buying English newspapers and magazines. Blaring out greetings like trumpet blasts, delivered with a jolly smile from the women and a doff of the hat from the men.

Never anything apologetic or deferential about them.

Days when there was a meet in town we'd hang around them like little peasants: will I howld the horse for ya sir, we'd say, hoping to have a couple of pence dropped into our hands. Looking up at them, like the poor man in the Bible story, waiting for crumbs to drop from the rich man's table. Prepared to make a show of grovelling if it meant being rewarded with the price of an ice-cream.

Never too cheeky, never overly deferential.

Everybody referred to Canon Haythornthwaite as the 'Protestant minister.' There was an eccentric air to him, with his grey hair and wild, bushy eyebrows. But the strangest thing of all was that he had a wife. A tubby, tweedy little wife. They rode along together in a big old tank of an Austin Cambridge, the Canon peering out through the spokes of the steering wheel. The wife sitting serenely beside him, smiling benignly. Like the gentry he lived at the end of a long bumpy driveway, in a big house fronted by a gravel sweep and a vast lawn surrounded by ancient trees noisy with crows. A couple of mares standing under broad elms swishing tails. And bullocks, big and summer-sleek, grazing contentedly in paddocks.

Soon after Jim's suggestion we were eyeing the high stone wall that surrounded the Rectory orchard and kitchen garden. Maybe ten feet in height it wound along the edge of the Saucestown road. So we had to get over it quickly before someone came along. Only trouble was the top of the wall had been spiked with jagged bottle ends. All colours: green, brown, blue, clear. But pointed bottle ends would not deter us once we'd caught sight of the tantalising display of apples and pears ripening in the summer sun. The forbidden fruit.

Once inside it seemed to me that we'd stolen into a Garden of Eden.

All around there was rich growth: trees, shrubs, vegetables, flowers. There were sagging rows of green beans supported by bamboo canes. Cracking the pods revealed fresh green peas, small, succulent. In a sunny spot by the wall a glasshouse stood with tomatoes gleaming amongst green foliage. We sampled everything. There were strawberry beds covered by nets, and blackcurrants, and raspberries. Perfectly formed heads of pale-green lettuce, fresh, delicate, grew in beds of rich clay. Not a weed to be seen.

Onions, scallions, carrots, parsnips, beetroot, all plump and healthy, unlike the ones that had to compete with a wilderness of weeds in our plot.

The pear trees were tall, ripe fruit at the top where the sun's heat caught it early. Jim had scampered high into the branches, was shoving pears inside his jumper. Beautiful luscious pears, some a delicate, yellow hue, dissolving pleasurably on the tongue, others dark, canvas-coloured. Nobody wanted to go for apples, so soft and juicy were the pears.

A gnarled, mossy old plum tree towered in a corner of the garden. Its fruit purplish, but not ripe enough yet. None of us wanted a griping pain in our stomachs.

Never had I been in such a place. Everything was so well-ordered, so proper, in its place. A deep quietness, a Sunday-like solemnity pervaded as I moved along its winding gravel paths edged with sweet-scented flowers and shrubs.

Still, my instinct was for caution as I moved away from the others, fearful of being caught, yet drawn on by curiosity and the lure of winding pathways that I felt would lead me on to some secret place, to some kind of revelation or discovery. I passed under pink and red rambling roses entwined on an arched metal frame. The path led to a little fountain with water tinkling from cherubic figures – and just beyond it a kind of bower with masses of intertwined flowers suspended overhead on larch poles. I sat beneath them for a moment on a rustic seat, pondering black-painted words carved into a piece of wood:

'Thou hast a Garden for us, where to Bide.'

I repeated the words, liked their sound, felt vaguely consoled by them without understanding why.

A path of bumpy flagstones wound from the bower to a cone-shaped summer house at the centre of the garden.

Bees hummed busily amongst the flowers overhead, birds twittered and flitted about in the trees, the fountain tinkled. Butterflies floated silently in and out of the summer house. Swallows skimmed low through open spaces.

The furtive, muted sounds of the gang carried from high in the pear trees.

The sergeant, Lacey, Virgilius, Paudie's absence, our camp, everything seemed far away and not so important in the strange peace that permeated this garden. It was almost like being in a church, only better – there were no blank-faced statues with eyes turned heavenward, no garish holy pictures to trouble the mind in the tranquil air of the Protestant minister's garden. Virgilius had always hammered into us the need to be quiet and respectful and genuflect in the church because, he said, of the Real Presence. Now, that's where you'll find the Real Presence, he said, in the church, in the tabernacle.

I'd always felt uneasy about all that.

There in the garden laid out by the Canon and his predecessors it was different. It seemed to me that being in this garden was like being in the presence of something, something felt, but not seen, and not like the Real Presence in the church. The Canon would probably come in the evenings and sit where I was seated, reading his office, at peace in the opaque tranquility all around.

I thought of the parish priest's house hidden within its grim grove of almost black evergreens, him striding up and down palefaced, frowning under his biretta, hands behind his back fingering a rosary.

Just then I heard a gate squeak. I flew back along the path.

'Quick, quick, there's someone coming,' I called, gesticulating into the pear tree.

There was an immediate panicked rustling of leaves and shaking of branches as everyone dropped earthwards. In seconds Jim was leading a scramble up the wall and over, cursing the pointed bottle ends.

Judo and I were last, as usual.

Just as we were about to start up the wall the Protestant minister appeared with Gundy Moran, his gardener, who'd come with him from his last parish – or whatever it was that minister's had. Gundy had a gimp and a Dublin accent. He'd got the gimp in the trenches.

'What are youse doing here, ye little gurriers?' he shouted.

We abandoned our attempt at escape. Turned to face the music.

The Protestant minister had a puzzled, kindly look on his face.

'Are you boys responsible for this?' he asked, regretfully, indicating the squashed pears and scattered twigs left in the wake of the departing gang.

'We're not, father,' I said.

'Don't be calling him father, he's not a father, he's a reverend, call him your reverence,' Gundy said, clipping me on the back of the head.

'Now, now, no need for that Thomas, it's ok, it's quite all right,' the Canon said.

'It's not all right, reverend,' Gundy, the gimpy aul' cripple said, 'you'll have to get the sergeant onto these boyos.'

The sergeant.

Jaysus, I thought, looking at Judo.

191

'Oh, we'll see, we'll see,' said the Canon, 'first though we had better get this mess tidied up, Thomas, fetch a barrow from the shed, like a good fellow.'

'Me, is it me? It's them lads should be doing that – not me!'

'I'm sure they'll be willing to lend a hand, won't you boys?'

'Oh, we will father, your reverence,' we chorused, eagerly.

Gundy did a lot of muttering and raked us with dirty looks as we tidied up.

Afterwards the Canon brought us through the back door and into the Rectory kitchen. Mrs. Kane, the housekeeper, was at the table in a large apron, kneading a lump of dough.

'Ah, good afternoon, Mrs.Kane, perhaps you could find some of your delicious buns for these boys?'

Mrs. Kane intimated with a murderous look that she could, indeed, find buns, but that it would give her no great pleasure to do so.

The Canon disappeared.

'What were them little whelps up to?' she asked Gundy, who was hovering indignantly in the doorway.

'Only robbing the best pears in the orchard, *and* the bleeding strawberries, we'll be lucky if there's any ripe ones left for the country markets Friday morning!'

'An' *he's* giving 'em buns for their trouble, if ya don't smile,' said Mrs. Kane.

'A good trimming is what them young lads should get, then straight down to the sergeant, that'd soften their cough fairly lively,' said Gundy.

'Proper order,' said Mrs. Kane.

'Now, here we are boys, I knew they were in the pantry,' said the Canon, coming back with two bottles of O'Brien's lemonade.

'I like to keep a little something in reserve, a special treat for my grandchildren,' he said, as he yanked the tops off.

Grandchildren?

A minister with grandchildren?

How could that be? I wondered, glancing at Judo.

He shrugged, tilted his head and took a deep draught of

192

lemonade.

Mrs. Kane's glare would have melted the icing on the buns – if we weren't intent on scoffing them down so quickly.

Judo kicked me under the table. This was us hitting the jackpot.

'Did you make them up, father, I mean your reverence, the words at the seat – on the piece of timber?' I asked.

'Oh, you saw that did you?' he said, pleased.

'I'm afraid I didn't, ah, make them up, I borrowed them from a poem of George Herbert's, he was English, a minister like me, except he wrote beautiful poems, you know, so very beautiful, those words are from a particular favourite of mine called *The Flower*,' the Canon said.

He was silent for a moment, gazed out the window. But not at anything, just like the mother did sometimes. Gazing at nothing but seeing something that we didn't see.

'Was a priest ever a poet, father?' Judo asked.

'He's reverend… not father ya thick,' Gundy said, still hovering in the doorway.

'It's quite all right, Thomas, an innocent mistake, well, yes, yes, there was Hopkins, he was a Jesuit you know, and a very fine poet,' said the Canon.

None of the names meant anything to me.

'Do the words mean that God has a garden in heaven, for us when we … you know… like?' I asked.

'Kick the bucket, is it?' Gundy butted in again.

'Hadn't you better check on the bees, Thomas?' said the Canon.

Gundy limped away grumbling.

'Pass on, you mean? Well, I like to think that we will all have beautiful gardens to walk in when we get to heaven, gardens far more beautiful than mine, one is always close to God in a garden, I believe,' the Canon said, smiling.

He was a kind man, the Canon.

When we left the kitchen I could feel Mrs. Kane's eyes driving daggers deep into my back.

A short time later we were sliding onto the shiny, leatherette seats of the Austin Cambridge and riding back home like kings. The sergeant was hauling his bike out the barrack door as we passed.

'Give him a wave, willya,' Judo said to me, waving madly at the sergeant.

'The sergeant's a friend of yours, it seems,' said the Canon.

'Shall I?' he asked, and tooted the horn at the sergeant.

Then waved with us.

The sergeant responded with his usual glare.

'He's kind of a friend, father,' I said, looking through the back window of the Cambridge as the scowling sergeant grew smaller in the distance.

When the Cambridge drew up outside our house astonished faces appeared over half-doors and Jim peered in disbelief from behind the curtain of our kitchen window.

Bottles of lemonade, home-made buns, a spin in the Protestant minister's Cambridge: Mamie Croke and Josie Barratt would ply us with questions for days. But more importantly, the rest of the gang would be ravaged by envy.

# 38

# Foxy Bourke

Saturday morning and I was sitting on the stile opposite our front door. Dallying under a blue sky before going to the camp. Judo had called earlier but I'd wanted to finish reading *White Fang*. I was stuck in it every evening now when the gallivanting was done and we were all at home sitting around the kitchen. Locked into our own little comic or library book worlds. Radio humming on the shelf. The mother nodding by the fire, sewing patches onto trousers, darning socks. The father out somewhere or stretched in the Morris Minor car seat reading the paper.

'Tis time ye were heading off to bed lads,' the mother'd say.

'Can I just read one more page,' Jim would say.

Lost in *The Count of Monte Cristo*.

'Can I have a cut o' bread Mammy?' Gerry would ask.

'No, 'twill only keep you awake, anyway we need it all for the breakfast,' she'd say, yawning.

'But I'm starving Mammy.'

'Off with ye now,' she'd say.

Silently we'd resist. Continue reading through drooping eyelids.

'Will ye go to bed will ye,' she'd say once more, sharply this time.

Reluctantly we'd leave off reading to go to bed, always anxious to get back to reading, to re-enter that fictional world.

I had been drawn right into the frozen wastelands of Alaska and the story of *White Fang*, a wolf brought in from the wild and tamed by humans. They hadn't broken his spirit, though. He allowed himself to be harnessed to a sled, responded to their urgings when on the trail. But they couldn't break his wolf-spirit. Inside he was still pure wolf.

I sat there on the warm stone of the stile, the sun blazing, mind full of idle, unconnected thoughts, not in any hurry to head for the camp. It was different there now without Paudie. Even if mostly he used to just boss me around. It didn't matter what we did there as long as we were *there*, lazing around in our own world. Only, I was beginning to realise that when we didn't have adults bossing us around, we just tried to boss one another. But Judo and I never got to boss anyone, so whereever we were there was always someone bossing us. Virgilius, the sergeant, the father, Paudie and Horse, every one of them got a turn at bossing us.

Even so the camp was still our refuge.

It was nice, sitting there on the wall, the heat of the sun on the back of my neck. Lazily wondering if I should slide to the ground and head off to the camp, or go back inside and continue reading *White Fang*. I might end up getting jobs to do if I did that, though. I remained where I was feeling no compulsion or desire to do anything other than sit and gaze. I looked along the row of houses. Pad Power hadn't appeared at his half-door for a gawk during all the time I'd been sitting there. That was unusual for him.

I turned my gaze down The Valley and to the east. Sliabhnamon looked bigger, clearer, in the morning sunshine, seemed to have edged closer to the town.

Foxy Bourke was coming up Mulligan's Hill, on his way home from the creamery. The obstinate-looking jennet striding along as usual, head high, ears pricked, looking ahead, striving towards something visible only to him.

Foxy leaned backwards on the reins when he saw me, managing to stop the jennet opposite where I was sitting.

The jennet didn't approve. He shook himself. The draught-chains rattled. He chomped on his bit, nodded his head impatiently. Looked at me with, wild, dilated eyes.

Foxy held him, keeping a tight pull on the reins.

We talked in an aimless way about comics. I told him about my sixty-four pagers. He said he had loads of Commando sixty-four pagers at home – would I like to come out to his house for a gawk?

I hesitated. I'd never hung around with Foxy. He was always

196

lurking on the margins, not seeming to belong anywhere. Not fully accepted by any of the town gangs. I'd never been out to his house. He was older than me. The only person I hung around with was Judo. And I'd only been in his house once, for a few minutes before his mother had driven the two of us back out the door at the end of a sweeping brush.

But the lure of those sixty-four pagers was too much. I climbed onto the cart. It was a box-cart with tailboard removed. There was only one churn, a big twenty- galloner with damp sacking underneath to keep it from sliding back along the cart as it rattled along. The separated milk for their calves sloshed and splashed inside.

I didn't remind Foxy of the day we'd ambushed him.

Foxy arsed over a bit, made room for me to sit with one buttock on the butterbox that served as a seat. I didn't feel comfortable pressed up against him like that. I leaned forward, elbows on my knees, minimizing the contact. I'd never felt like that when Judo and I were physically close together, when we were wrestling or when I was carrying him on my back. I'd never even thought about it. Having his body touch mine didn't feel like something that I wanted to avoid. But with Foxy I was conscious of his closeness as some form of intimacy that he wanted, or was trying to engineer. I began building myself up to escape by vaulting over the side of the cart. But I was distracted when I saw Mamie sitting in her kitchen as we passed. Seated at the table drawing on a Woodbine, a mug of tea in front of her.

'Howya, Mamie,' I called, anxious for her to see me on the cart.

But she seemed to be lost in a tense reverie.

'Look at feckin Ben Hur,' Paddy Harney growled sourly as we passed his door.

'Contrary aul' hoor,' Foxy said.

The jennet moved quickly along reacting with pricked ears, raised head and sideways gait to every piece of paper shifting on the road or bird flittering in the ditches.

'He's a right aul' sooner,' Foxy said, chucking on the reins.

Once or twice Foxy put his hand on my shoulder and my knee to get my attention. He would point something out to me, something that could be seen from the vantage point of the cart. His pudgy hand seemed to linger a fraction too long and I didn't like it. It seemed more calculated than spontaneous touching.

Foxy lived with his father on a miserable farm about a mile outside the town, just beyond an ancient graveyard with lopsided headstones and tall scutch grass.

We went into the graveyard for a look around. Foxy tied the jennet to the branch of a lilac tree growing out over the graveyard wall. We wandered among ancient headstones standing in tall grass, trying to decipher chiselled inscriptions that had weathered away over the centuries. I wondered what was left in the ground underneath.

Foxy's mother had died when he was still very young. Because of that he seemed a bit more neglected looking than the rest of us. In need of something. He didn't have anyone to patch or sew his trousers when they were ripped by briars or barbed wire. As long as there wasn't a tear in the lining exposing bare flesh Foxy wouldn't be too bothered. If his flesh could be seen inside he would put some rough stitching in the tear himself.

When we reached the un-gated, ivy-covered piers that led into Bourke's yard the jennet swung right-handed unbidden. We were in a rectangular grass-covered yard. Hens scratched about at the base of a huge dungheap.

The dwelling house was long and low with an undulating roof that looked as though it might cave in at any moment. Slates were missing.

'No sign of the aul' fella,' Foxy said.

Calves bawled from beyond the house.

A sheepdog with lolling tongue appeared and moved wolflike around the yard, watching us. I called and coaxed but he remained aloof.

The farm was small, about thirty acres in size.

We carried the separated milk in buckets to calves that grazed in a small field behind the house populated with thistles, buachalainns and docks.

After that we went into a murky kitchen. Foxy's father wasn't there.

An enamel basin filled with dirty cups, saucers and plates stood on the table. There was big black range, cold and unlit.

'The aul' fella must be down in the bottom field,' Foxy said.

It seemed their cows were breaking through a bounds ditch into a neighbouring farm.

'It's the red heifer that does it, she's a lighting hoor,' Foxy said.

'Where's the sixty-four pagers?' I asked.

He rummaged inside the bottom press of a dresser and came back with a few old sixty-four pagers. The pages were tightly curled. Had been nibbled in places.

'For feck's sake, Foxy, is that all you've got, ya couldn't read them,' I said.

'I had more, the aul' fella musta used them for wiping his arse,' he said.

'Why doesn't he use old newspapers, that's what we do,' I said.

'We don't buy any papers,' he said.

'Well, he should use dock leaves then, or a fist of grass,' I said, annoyed with Foxy, feeling that he'd duped me into coming out with the promise of sixty-four pagers that he didn't have.

'We might be getting a telly,' Foxy said, quickly.

I looked around the kitchen. There wasn't much to see. Nothing on the walls except a Sacred Heart. The only uncluttered space was in front of the radio to give access to the control knobs. An apron hung on the back of the front door. It hadn't been taken down in a long, long time. I couldn't imagine a telly in this kitchen.

'The aul' fella said if I did all the jobs he'd probably get one soon, 'twould be grand on the winter nights,' Foxy said.

'For Christmas,' he added.

'We'll never get one,' I said.

Having a telly in our own kitchen seemed an unimaginable

199

luxury. It would mean no more standing on cold winter evenings at O'Shea's shop window trying to figure out what was happening in *The Twilight Zone* without sound. Mamie's half-door was kept shut on winter's evenings with sacks and old top coats piled at the foot – keeping in the meagre heat that came from the open fire.

Most evenings Foxy cycled into town when his father had gone to the pub. You'd see him hanging around on his own, as forlorn as a stray dog.

Better than hanging around this dump, I thought.

'You could watch *The Twilight Zone* and *The Naked City*,' I said.

'You could come out and watch it, if ya wanted to, just you though, not that Judo, he's too much of a smart aleck.'

'The aul' fella said the mother would never let one o' them things into the house if she was alive,' Foxy said.

I felt sorry for him, not having a mother and all. But I wasn't going to start hanging around with him in the hope that there was going to be a telly in this miserable kitchen.

'The mother died when I was only a baby,' he said.

I looked at the wall.

'It must be grand having a mother,' he said, 'the aul' fella couldn't cook anything, couldn't even boil an egg.'

It had never occurred to me to think what life would be like without a mother.

'I better feck off home so,' I said.

'Don't go yet,' he said, 'come on down to the hen house, the aul' hen is after hatching, I'll show you the new chicks.'

I followed without any great enthusiasm. I wasn't interested in new-born chicks.

There was a ferocious racket coming from the henhouse.

'There's wan of them after laying,' Foxy said, explaining.

The henhouse was gloomy, criss-crossed with perches.

The newly-hatched chicks milled around the mother-hen, little yellowish pieces of fluff on orange coloured legs.

'They're only a day old,' Foxy said, closing the door.

He seemed anxious about something. He closed the door and ran the bolt.

I wasn't interested in the chicks. My mind was wandering towards the camp.

'Will we measure our mickeys, see whose is the biggest?' Foxy said suddenly, desperately.

I was stunned. Measure our mickeys – why the feckin hell would anyone want to do such a thing?

'For feck's sake, Foxy, no,' I said.

'C'mon, just for a laugh,' he said.

'I'm not measuring me mickey with anyone,' I said.

'I'll show you mine first,' he said, when I said nothing.

He began pulling his braces over his shoulders.

'I don't want to do it, I'm going home now Foxy,' I said.

He didn't move from in front of the door.

'What's going on in there?' a voice sounded from outside.

It was Foxy's father.

'Nothing, nothing, I'm only showing Jonno the new chicks,' Foxy called, dragging his trousers back up.

'Well hurry up, I've jobs for you to be doing,' he answered.

Through the slits on the home-made door I saw him walk across the yard towards the house. Wearing wellingtons, the tops turned down to ventilate his feet for the summer.

'I'll see ya Foxy,' I said, heading for the gate.

'Will ya come out again?' he asked.

'Maybe,' I said.

I looked back from the gate. He was in the middle of the yard cuddling the wolf-headed sheepdog. Looking lost, forlorn, vulnerable.

I set off along the road back to town. Stamping out the guilty feelings.

That Foxy, I thought, that fucken Foxy.

At the edge of town I left the road and headed across some fields until I reached the railway line.

'Who the feckin hell were ya with till now?' Judo asked as I came into the camp.

'Nobody,' I answered.

# 39

# Fallen Heroes

Mamie Mackey was listening to the match, radio going full blast. Mícheál O'Hehir's voice, hoarse, frantic with excitement, rising, falling with the rhythm of the game, came over the half-door in electrifying bursts – sending an invisible charge through the sleepy air of that Sunday afternoon. Compelling us to listen. Names flew like bullets past us as we paused, Judo and I, at the door: Carey, Doyle, Devaney, Kiely, Maher, McKenna, Wall.

Names burned like brands into our consciousness.

The mighty men of Tipperary, Mícheál O'Hehir called them.

But on that Sunday the mighty men were in trouble.

And Waterford men with unfamiliar names were the cause: Grimes, Condon, Power.

Who the hell were those lads, I wondered

'They're going to be bet, they're going to be feckin well bet,' Mamie said from the car seat, lighting another Woodbine.

She was seated as usual in the old Morris Minor car seat – but sitting forward, on edge.

This wasn't meant to happen. Our heroes weren't meant to be in trouble.

If it was Cork, yes, then it would be really hard, touch and go to the end, to the very last puck. But it wasn't. It was Waterford.

On the last Sunday in July. The Munster hurling Final. Tipp playing Waterford. Going for the three in a row. Tipp always won Munster Finals, especially when they were playing teams like Waterford.

For as long as I could remember, Tipp on the radio winning titanic hurling matches had been part of every summer. Mostly against Cork. No other games sent a charge through the summer air like Tipp and Cork.

Not today, though.

Mamie came to the door.

'Nothing but feckin wides in the first half, they're three points behind now and it nearly over,' she said, lighting another Woodbine with shaking hand.

Without a word Judo and I turned away, headed for the camp.

Paddy Harney was leaning on his half-door the match blaring from the radio behind his back.

'They're not so goddamn hot today, eh, they met their match today all right the sonsabitches, the mighty feckin men of Tipperary me arse,' he said.

A dart of resentment shot through me. Even though I hadn't been listening to all of the game, I'd assumed that it would be another routine day for our heroes in Blue and Gold. But now, when it seemed they were going to be beaten, Paddy's words sounded like betrayal.

'A sour aul' bastard,' I said.

'He's only a shaggin aul' Yank, sure what would he know about hurling?' Judo said. The sound of the game faded behind us as we moved on, then began to rise ahead of us again as we approached the cinema.

Men in white shirts, sleeves rolled up, were gathered round a transistor that seemed to vibrate on the steps of the cinema such was the intensity of what it was relaying. It was strange, seeing it, the tranny small on the steps, tall men, eyes fixed on it, the almost unbearable tension in the air around them.

They leaned over it, rigid, a kind of desperation in their poses. Trying to visualise what was happening in a field far away in Limerick. The Gaelic Grounds.

Where things were not going Tipp's way.

There on the steps, they willed their team on. Seeing in their mind's eye the dusty field, the packed, heaving crowds, the straining bodies in blue and gold.

'Ah, Jaysus, feck Devaney, an open goal.'

Bully, the bicycle man, straightened, skipped away, stamped, clapped his hands in frustration as the commentator described a series of misses by the Tipperary forwards. First came a surge of hope that had the men straightening in anticipation as Larry Kiely burst through onto the Waterford goal, this was it, Kiely had done

203

it before, they teetered on the verge of ecstasy, Tipp might snatch it at the end...

'C'mon, Kiely c'mon, will ya.'

'Let fly.'

'Bury it, bury the fucken thing.'

They picture Kiely in that far away field, letting fly, they straighten expecting a certain goal, but no, no, *Jaysus* no, he hits the post...

They groan, they wilt. The roar of the crowd intensifies until it seems the tranny must explode...

'For fuck's sake.'

'Ah Jaysus.'

'No, no, no,' O'Hehir screams in disbelief, 'but wait, wait a minute, the sliotar rebounds towards Donie Nealon...'

Nealon has it, he must score, it must be a goal...

Again they straighten, grip one another, tense with expectation, waiting to erupt, imagining Nealon's action, willing the sliotar to the net ...

NEALON STRIKES.

But no, no, no, it flies back off the other post...

They are deflated, desperate once more...

'Ah Mother a Jaysus.'

'What the feck is wrong with ye?'

... but wait, wait it comes to Liam Devaney, in front of an open goal.

The men grab one another prepare to celebrate, hope revived, this is it, it has to be, because Devaney never misses, they are almost in the act of jumping, clenched fists punching skyward, they can see the net shaking...

Devaney whips first time. Unbelievably the sliothar flies over the bar.

'Dear, oh dear, it's over the bar, it's a point, a point for Tipperary,' O'Hehir says, emphatically, with finality.

They slump in dejection, hope snatched away, dreams destroyed, limp, spent from the almost unbearable tension and excitement that has ravaged them in the final minutes of the game.

The match ends.

'Oh what a game, what a game,' O'Hehir shouts, 'here at the Gaelic Grounds it ends Waterford eleven points, Tipperary eight, and the All-Ireland champions are beaten and out of the championship.'

A mini-hurricane of voices roars in one continuous cacophony of sound from the radio. We are beaten. Gone. The mighty men of Tipperary, banished. Out of the championship.

Tom switches the tranny off. There is silence, we readjust, come back to the world around us again, hear other sounds: crows on the wires overhead, voices from the cinema.

Everything within me droops, dies. I hadn't listened to most of the match, I'd only heard the last fifteen minutes or so. I'd been looking forward to *Pick of the Pops*, but now, now it didn't matter.

The men are silent for long seconds, speechless, look at one another in shock, then all talk at once, bewildered, trying to make sense of it.

'Fucken Kiely should have buried it...'

'Too much made of that fella.'

But shur Nealon...'

'And as for that Devaney...'

'No, no, no, Kiely should have buried it the first time.'

They range back over the happenings of the game. Talking, talking, going over and over the same detail, like a bereaved person going over the last hours of their beloved's life. Eventually they separate, walk away.

Tipp's summer of hurling is over.

We go on to the camp, subdued.

Later, after the devotions, Judo and I linger on the steps of the church.

Every summer Sunday evening there is a gathering of men outside the church after the devotions. They meet to discuss the day. Especially hurling and football matches. Club and county. The shock and disbelief from earlier in the day has been replaced by anger.

'They'll be no three in a row now,' says Bully the bicycle man.

'They're not a patch on the forty-nine team, not a patch.'

'They lost it on the line.'

205

'Leahy should uv made changes, sure Doyle is past it, gone.'

'There's not another All-Ireland in that team…'

On they go, couching their disappointment in criticism of players, selectors, referee: they should have taken this lad off, put that lad on, this lad should have been switched, another fella shouldn't have started. On it went for ages until Duffy, the Cork man who lives in Kerry Street, came unsteadily along the far side of the street.

'Christ would ya look at who's coming,' Jack Ryan says.

Duffy stops. Puffs himself up. Beams over at the gathering.

'That Tipp'rary team ud bate nothing,' he shouts.

'Nothing, that's what they'd bate, a crowd of aul' women, they wouldn't bate eggs.'

'We bet ye, didn't we,' Bully shouts back.

'They wouldn't bate pussy, so they wouldn't, where's yeer three in a row now, hah?'

'We'll be back,' says Bully.

'That's what Napoleon said and he running outa Moscow,' Duffy shouts.

Bully, all of them, are sickened into silence.

'What about the three in a row now, hah, yeer gone, shagged, 'tis gonta be a long summer for ye, and a longer winter, c'mon the Deise.'

He moves off, a Corkman shouting for Waterford.

A few minutes later he turns as he is about to go in to the Bridge Bar.

'G'wan the Blood and Bandage,' he roars.

They have no answer now, they can only endure. Another long winter will have to pass before there is a chance of redemption.

Later as we make our way down past the Bridge Bar to sit on the cinema wall we hear Duffy singing ecstatically inside:

'Hooow oft do my thoughts in their fanceee take flight/ to the home of my childhood awaaaay.'

Cork haven't won anything, but neither have Tipp.

# 40

# The Fit-Ups

I was in the camp sitting on a stone reading an old *Beezer*. Gotten in a swap with Philly Landy. It was tattered, marked with jam and tea stains. The bottom of the Colonel Blimp page had been torn off and I was left wondering what exactly he'd ended up doing to his dog, Rover, after he'd mistaken him for an escaped lion.

Philly was looking over my shoulder, taking it upon himself to explain how the page had come to be torn and what Blimp had accidentally done to his dog. If I couldn't read it myself I definitely didn't want to listen to Philly telling me about it. Spraying me with spittle. Turning the one-page story into a stuttering epic.

I told him to feck off and not be spitting on the back of my neck. Over he wandered to Judo who was winding up the gramophone to play Count John McCormack. For the twentieth time.

'Don't play that feckin thing again, Judo, I'm sicka hearing it,' I shouted.

'Shag off,' Judo said.

He dropped the needle onto the record and Count John began singing as though from the bottom of a barrel:

'On yonder hill there stands a maiden,

who she is I do not know,

I shall court her for her beauty,

She must answer yes or no.'

Judo skipped and capered to the chorus.

'Oh, no John, no John, no.'

'Eejit,' I shouted.

Just then Jim came bursting from the briary tunnel that led from the railway line in to the camp.

'Hey, hey, there's a loada caravans after pulling up outside the

Town Hall,' he said.

He'd been up to Newport's paper shop to buy *The Beano* because he had eight pence to spend.

The mention of something out of the ordinary had us on our feet straight away, a sudden surge of energy banishing the ennui that had been weighing down on us, heavy as lead.

Caravans outside the Town Hall could mean only one thing: a travelling show.

There was no need for a consultation, we abandoned the camp straightaway and ran off to investigate.

'Jaysus look,' Jim said.

A tall man was stepping out of the Bridge Bar. Unlike any man that we'd ever seen before. Judo pulled me to a halt and we stood and gawked at him. He was aloof, mysterious. In his grey pinstriped suit, the kind gangsters wore, he seemed like someone from a film. Edward G. Robinson. Or George Raft. Only a lot taller than either of those. He had white cuffs that reached to the knuckles of each, long-fingered, creepy-looking, hand. A large gold-coloured cufflink adorned each cuff. A pink cravat shone from inside his shirt collar. He was smoking a cigarette. And wearing make-up. That really made me stare. A man wearing make-up. Jaysus. Shadow around his eyes, tan caked onto his face.

'For feck's sake, he's half a woman,' I said to Judo.

His hair was long, slicked back behind his ears. Probably with Brilliantine. It grew out over his shirt collar, curling upwards, reminding me of Kit Carson, the top scout in the Wild West.

I wondered if that was the hairstyle of a shaggin poet the kind the father was determined we should never have.

He walked ahead of us along the street drawing heavily on his cigarette, eyes fixed on the footpath. He didn't return the salute he got from Luggy Leahy— who turned and looked after him.

'A quare looking hawk, that fella,' he said to us.

The man in the suit was oblivious to all around him, seemed to be absorbed in deep, dark thought. I had never seen anyone so completely taken up with their own thoughts.

Willie Stapleton, the cobbler, came to the door of While-U-

Waits' shoe repair shop to have a look at him. His curiosity was rewarded with a moment of drama.

The man in the suit stopped abruptly outside the post office and slammed his cigarette onto the footpath. Crushed it under a patent leather shoe. Moved on quickly then, and more purposefully.

We looked at one another.

'Jaysus,' Judo said.

It was so dramatic that later on I recreated it at home in the kitchen for the mother's benefit: walking along puffing an imaginary cigarette, slamming it to the blackened floor.

Wearing my version of an anguished expression.

Judo poked at the remnant of the cigarette, examined it closely. We both did, stared at it like Sherlock Holmes and Watson, as if it should yield up some information about the man in the suit. It didn't – other than telling us that, Jaysus, he was wearing some kind of lipstick as well and could have got a few more drags from it. We followed him. When he came to the caravans outside the Town Hall he pushed a door open, stooped and went inside. The caravan creaked slightly as he moved around. Almost immediately a woman's voice rose, whining on every word. The man did not respond. Judo and I moved closer, to a window where the curtains were parted and peeped in. The man was seated and smoking again, hunched, head resting on one hand in a posture of resignation. The woman was out of our view but the sound of her voice went relentlessly on. I wondered what was going on in there. The man looked up. His eyes met mine for an instant. The dull desperation in those eyes startled me – and the defeated look on his made-up face. He didn't look at all like the man I'd seen on the street only minutes before. He rose and snapped the curtains shut.

There wasn't much to be seen on the street, just four pretty large caravans parked in a row parallel with the footpath. We'd had show people here before putting on revues and sketches in the Town Hall. We weren't quite sure what group this was. The name didn't bother us though - we were interested only in the distraction the shows would provide.

We hung around the Hall door, keeping an eye on the caravan hoping for some development in the unseen drama that I sensed was going on in there. Nothing happened. All was silent. Two men were carrying costumes and scenery flats through the door and up the stairs. With no great enthusiasm.

'Are ye putting on a show tonight?' Judo asked.

'I suppose so,' one of them said.

'What time will it be at?'

'Around eight, I suppose,' he grunted.

We headed back to the camp.

At half-seven there was a queue of sorts on the street outside the Town Hall waiting for the doors to open. A mixture of adults and children.

Country people had cycled in to town for the show. Had thrown their bikes against the wall of the building. Bridgie Burke was in from Ballinard. Her laugh pealing and echoing all along the street. Men leaned casually against the building, smoking, caps slanted onto their foreheads against the lowering sun. Some boys who had cycled in from Tullamaine were watching from the steps of the bank on the far side of the street. Keeping clear of the townies, and keeping an eye on the door of the Town Hall. I recognised Bobby Ryan who had sat beside me for a while in fourth class. I'd gotten a loan of his bike a few times to cycle home at lunch-time. I reckoned he'd surely have some money for sweets and decided to go to him during the interval to cadge a few.

Three men with nothing much to do were seated on the cool limestone blocks of the Chair watching the people queue for the show. There was little else for them to watch other than long shadows from the west that were creeping up a near-empty Main Street. Mary Dunno from the Green was there. Once the show got going she would be shouting warnings to people on the stage, just as she did to the characters in films at the Capitol cinema. Ringo from the estate gang was going around singing 'The Goochy Goo.' Over and over.

'Can anybody tell me what's the Goochy Goo, the Goochy Goo...'

The song had been playing incessantly on the radio for a number of weeks.

Finally we paid our money and pounded our way up the blackened, ancient stairs and into the main hall. Across the floor we rushed pushing chairs out of the way as we made for the old church pew placed against the back wall, jostled and pulled one another off trying to get the best position. This was our favourite spot. The prize was to be able to sit up on the backrest and have a view across the heads of the audience. Sitting there we felt gave us a licence to shout and heckle whenever we pleased.

The hall was less than half full with the crowd packed into the seats closest to the stage. Except for us on the messers' seat at the back. The rows of empty chairs that lay between us and the main bulk of the audience made us feel detached and separate somehow – that we weren't bound by the same rules as the others. We elbowed one another, laughed insanely at one another's comments. Got disapproving looks from further up the hall. None of the priests or brothers was here so we were uninhibited. There would have been deferential looks and a bit of a strain had the parish priest been there.

The hall buzzed and crackled with expectation. Something different was about to happen, something that would colour the dullness for a while. Everyone talked and chatted, shifted chairs; boys moved from seat to seat, ate sweets, flicked the balled wrappers at one another, ran up and down the stairs to the toilets, annoying the people on the door who had to keep track of those who'd paid.

At last the curtains were drawn jerkily open and the music struck up. Five people were wedged together onstage singing and dancing.

'Another opening, another show, another opening, another show, the curtains up, and away we go, another opening of another show.'

On the right side of the stage a man in black trousers and

211

sequinned, glittering jacket played an electric guitar. Wearing a red fez and a goofy expression. I knew straightaway that he was going to be the funny guy. There was always a funny guy. So we watched him closely and waited for the laughs. On the left of stage another man, small and potbellied in a tuxedo and red cummerbund, played a saxophone. Separating them across the stage were three women, wearing black, fishnet nylons with seams, attempting a kind of Can-Can, legs swinging almost in unison. But not quite. First left, then right. Stage groaning under them. They began to falter as the music went on. The woman in the middle was heavily made-up and looked older. She seemed to be carried along on the interlinked arms of the other two. It required a tremendous effort on her part to keep time. The makeshift stage shook and creaked. When the singing and dancing stopped she sucked in air.

We shouted, stamped out feet. Judo did his wolf-whistle.

They sang two more songs with some wisecracks and Paddy the Irishman jokes in between from the funny guy with the fez. They finished with 'The Rhythm of Life.' The saxophone player took the lead and the three dancers were almost propping one another up by the time it ended.

The curtains closed after that. The little man in the tux and cummerbund came down and played an organ situated in front of the stage beside the drummer while some frantic activity went on behind the curtains. There was whispering, bumps, bulging of the curtains. The stage was being set for the next scene. I watched, wondering what would be revealed when the curtains were dragged open once more.

What followed was a sketch of 'The Croppy Boy,' a ballad that we'd been taught at school.

The funny guy with the fez was now the Croppy Boy seeking confession. Looking comical in three-quarter length pants, braces and knee socks. And a waistcoat decorated with shamrocks. Every move on stage was exaggerated. Especially the croppy's confession which silenced us all, had us in tears. Almost. Especially the bit about cursing three times since last Easter day and forgetting to pray for his mother's rest.

Every one of us had knelt penitently before the priest, just like the Croppy Boy, and the sanctity of the confessional had been hammered into us. So when Fr. Green jumped from behind the makeshift confessional screen, flung off his cloak and was revealed as a redcoat we booed, whistled, stamped our feet, at the absolute treachery of the English oppressor. Those Protestants didn't believe in confession. Fr. Green who'd become the redcoat was the man we'd seen hopping his cigarette on the street only now he was sporting a huge false moustache which resembled the handlebars of a bike and sagged perilously to one side. He stalked across the stage in high boots brandishing a sword. The croppy fell to his knees with bent head as the redcoat towered over him sword poised to strike his head off. The curtains closed as he swung the sword downwards. A great thump on a drum signified that the croppy's head had been struck from his body.

We jeered and clapped, enthralled by the drama of it all.

The funny guy came from behind the curtain to announce that there would be an interval now with tickets on sale for a raffle. We weren't interested in raffles. We wouldn't spend money on something like a feckin raffle ticket.

The country boys clattered downstairs together, heading for May Goode's sweetshop just down the street from the Town Hall. This would be my chance to cadge sweets from Bobby. He came back with an unbelievable luxury: a packet of Rolos – but refused to part with any. For the remainder of the show my thoughts strayed enviously to the Rolos as I pictured Bob easing them slyly from his pocket, savouring them slowly until they were all gone. I could almost taste the chocolate and toffee dissolving on my tongue.

When the stage had been re-arranged behind closed curtains once more the man in the suit and curling locks walked onstage, this time wearing black trousers and sparkling jacket. He sang 'The Goochy Goo.' His humour seemed to have improved greatly since I'd seen him through the curtains earlier in the day.

We sang madly, stamped along with the chorus.

The guy in the red fez came out again with his guitar and sang parodies of songs like 'Galway Bay.' Sometimes he'd stop when our laughing and catcalling became too raucous.

'Yeer only a shower of Mullinahone Teddy boys,' he'd shout towards us.

'We're not from Mullinahone ya feckin eejit,' Judo shouted back.

This got a big laugh and the fez man kept it going for about five minutes, like in a panto.

Next came another weepy sketch called 'My Little Grey Home in the West.'

Acted out silently in front of a flat at the back of the stage. It depicted a mountain scene with a winding road in the foreground leading to a little cottage with smoke curling from its chimney. The tottering dancer from earlier was seated in an armchair dressed as an old woman complete with shawl and rosary beads. The man on the organ played 'My Little Grey Home in the West' with a million heart-wrenching twirls. The old woman rose from her chair and shuffled tearfully towards the wings. A hand appeared holding a letter. She read the letter, walked around the stage kissing and clasping it to her breast. She then sat into the armchair and began saying the rosary. The guy with the fez came in carrying a bundle tied to a stick like the happy wanderer returning from his travels, gazed rapturously at the old lady in the chair. We roared laughing. But when he touched the old woman her head fell forward: she was dead. We exploded as the man with the make-up strolled onstage and sang the song through, he and the organ player rising to a dramatic crescendo as the curtains closed. Cheering and sustained foot stamping followed.

The man in the fez came out again with his guitar and played a medley of the Shadows hits as a climax to the show: 'Foot-tapper,' 'Apache,' 'Kon-tiki.' He finished by singing and playing 'The Young Ones.' I didn't really like Cliff Richard but stamped and sang along anyway.

Then we were running down the stairs and out into the last of the evening light. Judo and I sat for a while on the wall beside the cinema, the sound of Doris Day singing about the Deadwood stage acomin' on over the hill booming out behind us as we talked about the show.

Every afternoon at around three o'clock the Goochy Goo man would make his way to the Bridge Bar without exchanging a word or a look with anyone. He'd make his way back to the caravans at around five thirty, always smoking a cigarette. Always morose looking. His progress always monitored from windows and shop doors. Apart from that not much was seen of the show-people.

For the rest of the week Judo and I had to be content with sitting on the steps of the bank watching a meagre scatter of people make their way into the Town Hall. We could hear the singing and the pounding of feet on the stage: the laughter, the catcalls.

We got to the show again on Sunday night, the last night, for a 'gala' performance which was pretty much the same as what we'd seen on our first night, except that the man in the make-up recited 'To Be or not to Be' and was helped along by some older lads who were learning Hamlet with Brother Albert in the secondary school.

On Monday morning the caravans were gone. There was emptiness everywhere for a few nights. We had re-adjusted our usual routine to go to the bank steps every evening during the week that the show people had been in town. We returned to our old habit of going to the camp in the evenings or sitting on the bridge for a while with the men of the town watching people make their way into the cinema.

And then home when darkness came.

# 41

# A Hate Wave

For two days the sun had blazed down on us from a blue sky. Not a rain cloud in sight. Men were going about with shirt sleeves rolled up. Except for Paddy the Racket who still clattered along on his horse and cart hunched up in his tattered old crombie top coat.

Tar was soft and sticky on the road. Dogs lay in the shade, tongues lolling. Only people moved about in the heat.

Every hump and gully of Sliabhnamon stood out clearly in the blinding sunshine. Seemed almost close enough to touch.

All the old people were complaining about the heat. Wondered when it was going to end. Not too many days before they'd been wondering when the rain was going to end. Now it was the heat. No matter what kind of weather came they would always wonder how long before it would pass.

Wet days, dry days, soft days, sunny days, windy days, frosty days, even pet days, they all brought some kind of weather for old people to complain about.

Mary Croke was leaning over her half-door. Body coat removed – her only concession to the heat.

'Wicked hate there,' she said to me.

Her skinny white arms with their network of horrible blue veins sticking out from the short sleeves of her blue blouse. Thin as straws.

'Arra, Mary you can't bate the bit o' hate,' Ellie Power said from her half-door, drawing on her dudeen.

She was allowed the luxury of leaning over the half-door because Pad had gone bobbing off to the Bridge Bar for a few Sunday morning large bottles. Would probably take in the toss school on his way home.

But she stayed behind the half-door, not stepping out into the

216

glare of the sun.

'Tis fierce, they're giving it to last for the week,' Mary Croke said, gloomily, as if it was some kind of sickness, 'sure we're not able for that kinda hate atall, atall.'

She turned and peered back into the gloom of the kitchen.

'Are ya going to give the day sucking on them aul' Woodbines, or what, can't ya feck off with yerself for a spin on the bike and not be sitting there looking into the fire like that?' she said to Jimmy, her brother.

I didn't hear any reply from Jimmy. His only refuge from his sister's tongue was the Bridge Bar for large bottles when he had enough money.

'They sez pigs sweat a terror in the hate,' Josie Barratt said, knowledgeably, from her half-door.

Ellie jetted a disdainful plume of smoke from the side of her mouth.

'How could pigs sweat?' I asked.

'Don't mind that one, avick, she's only making a feck outa ya,' Mary said.

'Oh, 'tis true, I'm telling ye, they're not able for the hate at all, I heard it on the wireless, so I did,' Josie said.

'Well the hate ain't having any effect on Tommy Drohan, and he's a right aul' pig if ever I saw one,' Ellie said with a nod in the direction of Tommy's house down the road.

We laughed. Even Mary Croke managed a humourless grimace.

'Mind ye don't get cramp in that spring water out at the Newbridge, and look out for eels, them thread eels is dangerous, if those lads wind around yer big toe yer in trouble,' Josie said.

I wasn't sure if she was joking or not. But I hated those wriggly little thread-eels and the way they'd stick to your leg sometimes.

It was Sunday and we were over the dinner. I was standing there listening to the old women chat, waiting for the others to come from the house and head for Newbridge.

We were heading for the river to cool ourselves. Eager to plunge into the spring-cooled water at the new bridge that spanned the river out on Grove estate. It wasn't a new bridge anymore, though. It had been fifty years before, when it was built. But everybody called it Newbridge now as if it were a proper place name. It was situated about two miles outside the town. A tidy walk in the heat.

A short time later we were walking out the Grove road, skirting along the edge of Grove estate. Wide rolling grassland stretched away to our left. Horses stood in the shade of broad elms, tails swishing flies away. Or belly-deep in the river, nuzzling the water. Grove House stood shimmering in the distance, aloof and inscrutable in the heat. Rectangular windows, long and dark. I imagined a mysterious figure standing in one of those dark spaces. Gazing out at the world, at us trudging along in the afternoon heat.

Grasshoppers clicked madly along both sides of the road. That's how it always was on sunny days: grasshoppers playing their monotonous accompaniment to those long burning days that sometimes came with the summer. We stopped frequently to sit on the grassy margin of the roadside. Hoping, hoping that a car or a pony and cart would come along, give us a lift. But there was little or no traffic.

We had often walked to Newbridge and back without meeting a vehicle of any kind.

That Sunday I was gasping for water before we were halfway there, torturing myself with thoughts of the well-spring in the field close to the swimming hole. The sun could blaze the heat of the Sahara down on us – it would never warm the waters of that spring. It would always be there, forever cool, forever refreshing.

Edged with green watercress, water pure and crystal clear.

Tiny bubbles streaming ceaselessly from between clean grey pebbles at the bottom of the spring, water coming from some cool place deep in the earth. Lying flat on your stomach to drink the ice cold water straight from the spring, feeling it deliciously cooling parched mouth and throat, was as near to bliss as I could imagine on a scorching hot Sunday in August.

The more I thought about it the thirstier I became.

When we came within sight of the spring Judo began staggering, pretending he was in a desert seeing a mirage. We'd seen a fellow do that in a film once.

'Water, water,' he gasped.

Jim tripped him into a clump of rushes.

'Boll*ix,*' Judo shouted.

When we got there I stayed last in the queue for water. Going last meant I could take my time because there would be no one behind kicking at my legs and moaning, hurry up, hurry up, for feck's sake willya *come on* I'm gasping.

I lay there, drank at my leisure. Didn't use cupped hands. Drank straight from the spring. Again and again. But nothing could recapture that first delicious feel of cold spring water lingering in my mouth, cutting the summer dust off my parched throat.

The others raced away through the rushes heading for the bridge, drawn by the sounds of splashing and shouting voices. Going to the swimming hole always became a race over the last few yards: being first to arrive on the riverbank to size up the people in the water, first to get togged out and spread your towel on the grass, first to dive into the pool, suddenly seemed very important once the bridge came into view.

'I see your arse,' Judo said, as I togged out, bending and twisting like a contortionist, trying to hold the towel in place with one hand, use the other to pull one pair of short trousers off and another old pair on as swimming togs. The mother had sewn a large patch onto the seat of the old one. I didn't mind though, 'cos it was only a swimming togs now. So there was no indignity in wearing it. Anyway, none of the boys at the swimming hole would have real swimming togs. Only girls had real swimming togs.

Judo ran off.

I heard the flat slapping sound and screams as Judo launched himself straight to the centre of the pool and hit the water belly first. Jim, Pony and Philly were already in the pool. They taunted Judo:

'A big bellybreaker.'

'Yer useless.'

'Look at yer belly, 'tis red, that was some bellybreaker.'

The sound of voices: laughing, shouting, screeching, calling, crying, the sound of hands, arms, legs, whole bodies, car tubes, slapping, parting, wading, hitting the water, churning it frothy-white, drowned out the grasshopper chorus and all other summer sounds.

I ran between sunbathers stretched on towels and launched myself head first into the pool. Saw Judo and Jim's upturned faces as I took off. Then suddenly felt the first cold shock as I hit spring water. And a gurgling silence when my ears filled as I plunged out of the sunlight, shot towards the bottom. A brief moment of panic. I wriggled, twisted in the murky mossy depths of the pool seeing what looked like disembodied, white legs, bodies and a million bubbles above, the moss streaming and waving like thick green rock star hair on the stones below, before I burst gasping through the surface of the swimming hole, back into a world of blazing sunshine and sudden noise.

I lay on my back, let the water bear me up, gazed at a jet-trail dissipating in the blueness above.

Horse just couldn't let us relax in the water. No, he had to get us working on a dam to deepen the pool. He wanted it really deep 'cos he was going to dive off the bridge, he said.

We raised it with mossy stones from the riverbed. Big stones first, smaller ones in between, then packed rushes against it to slow the flow of water over the edge. We left some escape holes to stop green, stagnant slime from forming.

A blond-headed man from Killusty waded into the pool, checking the depth. His sunburned shoulders red against the whiteness of his back. The water rose around him until his head was covered. He re-appeared gradually at the far side of the pool.

'Tis a good eight feet deep at the centre,' he declared, blasting water and snot from his nostrils.

Soon after that Horse went and stood on the parapet of the bridge, declaring that he was going to make a daring dive right into the middle of the pool. Eyes darting left and right, seeking affirmation.

'It's too dangerous Horse, it's not deep enough,' I said.

'You'll split yer skull, Horse,' Philly said.

'You'd need a feckin sledgehammer to do that,' said Judo.

Horse threw him a look that promised retribution.

'Yeer all windy,' he said.

'You'll be all right, young fella, as long as you dive well clear of the concrete apron,' the Killusty man said.

He paced, measured, walked with authority along the apron of concrete that came about six feet out from the base of the bridge. The water kicking white around his ankles.

'And mind ya don't hit yer head offa them big stones to the left there at bottom,' the Killusty man warned.

Swimmers and paddlers cleared the pool, stood, gazed up at Horse on the bridge. Sunbathers on the bank rose onto their elbows to watch. Judo, sitting on a towel tuning the tranny to the Light Programme, stopped and stared.

Sounds died away, suspense grew as everyone concentrated on what Horse was about to attempt, once more the grasshoppers could be heard and the gurgle of the water spilling over the dam.

Horse teetered and teetered on the parapet.

He seemed to relax then, turned to one side as though he was not going to do it after all, then suddenly launched himself from the parapet, hit the water head first at an acute angle, curved — and shot straight up, bobbing like a cork in the water. It was done in an instant.

A cheer went up.

Judo turned the volume up high on the tranny as the *Pick of the Pops* theme blared out, right on cue it seemed. Making the air vibrate with even more energy.

'Hi, there pop-pickers... Freeman boomed suavely.

The intense heat, sunburn, the inevitable walk home in the evening sun were all forgotten, pushed to the backs of our minds by the constant flow of music from the tranny.

Billy Fury came on singing 'In Summer.'

It was the perfect accompaniment to splashing about and lying on the riverbank on that sunny Sunday in August. Just lying there, looking up at the blueness above, cursing, shouting, getting annoyed and threatening those in the water a bit too loudly when occasional sprays of water hit your warm body.

And there was a song called 'Come On Home' from The Springfields that I didn't like.

Roy Orbison had dropped right down, didn't even get a play.

When it came to the Top Ten Freeman played them all.

The Crystals came on singing 'Da Doo Ron Ron' and two sisters from the Main Street stood on the bank, began clapping and singing along. Both had been lying in the sun. Big blotchy red patches of sunburn glared on the white of their arms and legs. Their long red hair swung, they laughed, and shouldered one another incredulously as if to say look at us, oh Jesus, look at us, oh the madness, the crackedness of it, aren't we mad entirely.

Elvis had dropped to number five with 'Devil in Disguise.' And Frank shaggin Ifield, the yodeller, had finally made way for The Searchers at number one: 'Sweets for my sweets, sugar for my honey...' poured out across the swimming hole and the rushy fields all around.

Then suddenly time had slipped by and it was five o'clock, Freeman was saying 'All right? Right? Stay Bright,' was gone for another week. There was the usual yawning emptiness when the music ended, a few long moments of re-adjustment.

It was mostly small children in the shallows now as the older ones lay on the bank, energy sapped.

Gradually people began gathering towels, heading into clumps of rushes or behind bushes to get dressed and trail slowly, wearily, away towards the road and the long haul home in the evening heat. The man from Killusty let the air hiss out of his gigantic tractor-tube and left. Soon there was only us and the red-headed girls from Main Street. It was quiet, just the water lapping to froth at the edge of the pool and gurgling over the dam. The girls from Main Street stepped onto the concrete apron and agonised for ages before launching themselves squealing into the water. I watched their long red hair float and darken on the surface of the water before being submerged.

I was reluctant to leave it was so magical there, as if for just those few precious moments the world had come to a standstill and nothing mattered, I didn't have to do anything just lie there on the solid earth, listen to the sounds of the water, see the blue sky above and Sliabhnamon beyond, rise on one elbow to gaze at the mysterious mansion in the distance, horses browsing under trees.

But it had to end, we couldn't postpone the journey home any longer and finally we set off, tired even before we started. The walk seemed never-ending, the heat from the evening sun intense as we streeled up the Wood Hill, past trees alive and echoing with the sound of birds. The sound of the Abbey bell calling people to evening devotions and Benediction rolled lazily out from the town, mingling with birdsong from the wood.

The Cliff Adam's Singers were just starting their mournful croon on the radio when we came complaining into the kitchen and threw ourselves onto chairs and forms. The mother was there, a big bowl of salad with lettuce, scallions and tomatoes sitting ready on the table.

'I suppose yeer leppin' with the hunger,' she said, smiling, her face luminous and soft as she gazed at us.

# 42

# Closing Of A Door

There was something the matter with Mamie. She'd gone away one day in a car, a small case in her hand. I was sitting on the stile opposite her door that day, watching as she went. She hadn't looked happy getting into Paddy Whyte's black Prefect. Wearing a hat. That didn't look good. I'd never seen Mamie wearing a hat. It was black with a small feather sticking out. Like a funeral hat. I waved to her as the car pulled away but she didn't look back, didn't look left, didn't look right. Just sat rigidly in the front seat. Suddenly turned in on herself. It wasn't like Mamie not to be looking around, taking everything in.

'She's gone to hospital,' the mother said, when I asked about her.

'She's not well this long time,' the father said.

The hospital was in Cashel. The mother mentioned a name. Hogan. Surgeon Hogan. She was going to be under surgeon Hogan. It didn't sound good to me, being taken in a car to hospital in Cashel to be under a surgeon Hogan.

'Oh, a great man, surgent Hogan is going to open her,' Josie Barrett said.

I tried to picture the hospital, and surgeon Hogan opening people. Opening Mamie. Tried to put a face on the unknown. Only grim, blurry images formed in my mind.

She'd gone to hospital on the Monday that the show people had arrived. I was aware of her absence without really thinking of her. Except in the evening sometimes when Judo and I wanted to watch a scary episode of *The Twilight Zone* on the telly and were afraid to approach the half-door without Mamie to placate her contrary brother. That was when we really missed her.

Sometimes I'd overhear the mother and father talking, their voices always low and sombre. I knew they were talking about

Mamie and could sense that something was seriously wrong. There had to be something badly wrong because nobody ever went to hospital. Women sometimes went and came back with babies. Children went to get their tonsils out. I couldn't think of any other reason why someone would go to hospital.

So why had Mamie gone?

Old people mostly died in their houses and were laid out in their beds with candles burning and beads entwined in their wrinkled hands. Mamie was old, but not *that* old. We'd gone to see Mrs. Grant from down the road when she'd died. Kneeling by the bed saying a prayer I'd kept my head down, afraid to look fully at her dead face. What I'd seen from between my fingers had petrified me.

Was Mamie going to die, I wondered, like Mrs. Grant?

Would Johnny shake holy water around her as she drew her final breath and pray to keep away the evil spirits that were trying to snare her parting soul for the devil, open the bedroom window to let her soul fly to God?

That's what Mrs. Grant's daughter had done.

I'd never thought of Mamie as being young or old. Mamie was just Mamie, beyond change, ever-present, fag in hand, elbows on the half-door gazing happily out on the world. Full of curiosity. A word for everyone passing her door. And always a kind word. She wasn't hard, or bitter, Mamie, when she smiled it always shone in her eyes.

She was like Sliabhnamon to the east, always there when we got up in the morning.

Mamie couldn't die.

She came back in the same black Prefect. But she wasn't the same Mamie. She didn't appear at the door for a couple of days.

When I heard the father say she wasn't going to do any good a kind of dread took hold of me.

'She have the lad,' Josie said to Judo and me, eagerly.

'What's the lad, Mam, Josie Barratt said Mamie has the lad?' I asked the mother.

'Never mind what that one says, she can't keep her trap shut

225

for a minute,' the mother answered.

'But what's the lad?' I asked.

Reluctantly then she told me what it was. She said 'cancer' with difficulty. Incurable, she said. The thought of it filled me with fear, this notion that a malignant thing called cancer was out there stalking all of us.

The first morning that I saw her back at the half-door I had to stop myself from looking away, so gaunt and pale and haunted had her face become. Great dark rings had formed under her eyes. Her glasses sat crookedly on her nose.

'Howya, young fella,' she said, smiling, a ghostly imitation of her once beaming smile. When I saw blood on her blouse, just under her arm, I wanted to turn and run far away from there.

'Any good flicks lately?' she asked.

I told her about *To Hell and Back* the Audie Murphy war film that I'd seen the previous Sunday.

'He's a bit on the butty side for my liking, that Audie Murphy,' she said, 'I'd rather Steve McQueen or Richard Widmark any day.'

Talking was a big effort for her. I felt uneasy, standing there at the half-door, was frightened of the unspeakable, deathly thing that I saw in her gaunt, haunted face. It was as if the Mamie I knew, that I'd seen going away in that Prefect had not returned. That surgeon Hogan had taken the life force from her, sent us back a mere ghost of the old Mamie.

From then on I was afraid to go to the half-door, not afraid of contrary Johnny, but afraid of Mamie, of kind, affable Mamie. My friend Mamie. I dreaded seeing her lying back in the Morris Minor car seat, breathing rapidly, barely able to acknowledge my presence at the door. At first she'd struggled to her spot at the half-door as always. But she could no longer fill the doorway with her presence as she used to do. Her shoulders sagged. She clung on to the rim of the half-door with bloodless hands and didn't remain there for very long. Soon she stopped coming to her old spot at the half-door. For a while she confined herself to the car seat in the kitchen. Finally, even getting to the car seat became too much. She stayed in her bedroom.

And I never saw her alive again.

Sometimes when passing the open door I'd hear her voice, weak and plaintive, calling to Johnny. And I'd run to the camp, run away, do anything to get the memory of that quavering voice out of my head. Because it was the sound of diminishment and defeat, of the happy and cheerful being drawn down, down, slowly, into the terrifying darkness of death. It terrified me to think that Mamie could see all those evil spirits gathering around her bed and know that she was about to die, about to run the gauntlet between Heaven and Hell.

Judo said, naw, 'twas just bull, sure his father had told him that when you died you were dead and that was it, a feed for the worms, all that stuff about souls and spirits was just mumbo jumbo from the priests to keep the people under their thumb.

Judo seemed uncertain though. As though he was using his father's words to ward off fearful thoughts of the devil and evil spirits. But what his father had said to him was even more frightening to me than the stuff about souls and spirits. That there was nothing, no walking in heavenly gardens after death.

The jubilee nurse called every day. The doctor called. The pale, saintly priest from the Abbey called most days, came back out wearing his purple stole. All of their faces black and dark as death. Every time someone called to Mamie's Josie Barratt's head telescoped out over her half-door as she tried to guess what was going on inside from their demeanour.

The mother said Mamie had been anointed and we were to keep away from the door and keep quiet on the road outside. I'd run past her door on my way to the camp or the river bank. Coming home in the evening I'd notice that the door was fully closed, sense that death was at work in there. Sometimes, late in the evening Judo and I would sit on the stile as darkness bled into and thickened the last light of day. Faint chinks of yellowish light glowed through the warped boards of the door. I'd never thought a closed door could look so ominous.

'Tis only a matter of days,' I heard the father tell the mother.

'What aged woman was she at all?' Ned, the milkman, inquired of my mother.

'Only fifty-three,' the mother answered.

Mamie was dead already, being spoken of in the past tense.

*Fifty-three.* It seemed an inconceivable number of years to have lived. *Fifty- three.* How could anyone be that old? Sometimes when old Ellie was in the kitchen she would talk of things that had happened *thirty* years ago as though it were only yesterday. It was scary. I couldn't imagine that I would ever have that number of years behind me.

She died, finally. I didn't go to see her laid out. Feared those evil spirits might still be hanging around.

But mostly I didn't go because the trappings of death terrified me: the undertaker, the holy water beside the bed, the black hearse, the gleaming coffin, the candles, the incense, the mournful prayers. Blackness everywhere.

I tried to think of her walking in a garden, a beautiful, heavenly garden like the one the Protestant minister had said God would probably have. But I couldn't hold it in my head: visions of coffins and graves and Mamie dead kept pushing it out.

It was a small funeral, I heard the father say.

'Sure there was only Johnny and the mother. Wasn't it a fright she went before the mother and she an invalid all those years?' our mother said.

'Ya couldn't kill that aul' rip,' the father said.

Then they began to trace her family origins. She was gone and this would be her epitaph: what was said of her in the short hours and days after her death. Then the never-ending silence of the grave.

I hated listening to people talking about her like that now that she was dead: puzzling out her origins, her cousins and connections. Getting her into context before forgetting her forever.

But she was gone and for a long time afterwards the silent space over the half-door gaped emptily at me every time I passed.

# 43

# Round up at Kiltinan Castle

'Wait for me, will ye,' I shouted.

Desperately. 'Cos I was last.

The nearest person a good twenty yards ahead. I hated being that far behind. Not quite cut off, but distant. Always trying to catch up.

My shout was ignored. Or unheard.

I thought of turning back towards the town – but the ones I wanted to be with were up ahead, and I loved going to Kiltinan. Well, I loved *being* in Kiltinan – the walking there and back didn't appeal to me at all.

But what would be the use of going back, just to mope around alone, thinking of what I was missing, wondering what was going on out at Kiltinan in my absence?

Usually Judo would be struggling along in the rearguard with me. Not today though. He was an emerging leader now, determined to keep at the head of the gang, pushing himself on as I began to slacken after a half mile or so.

This running everywhere was something I couldn't understand. Jim said it was because I was a useless effer and lazy as sin.

But who really wanted to be *first* to arrive in Kiltinan? – we'd been there so many times before. It wasn't as if it was a race to see who would be first to look on a New World or something, like Columbus. No, whoever was first would simply be first, that was it, no reward, no distinction. I couldn't see the point of so much striving just for that.

With Jim acting as gang leader now that Paudie was gone and Horse losing interest I'd thought that maybe there wouldn't be so much running. I was wrong. And the crepe-soled sandals I was wearing were squeezing on my toes with every step. I needed bigger shoes, but they wouldn't come until Jim got a bigger pair, then I'd inherit his. And he wouldn't be getting new ones until the Free Boot Scheme started when the schools re-opened in September.

So, every time they moved out of sight around a bend I forced myself to break into a run. Then just as I rounded that bend and slackened gratefully to a walk they disappeared once more around another bloody bend. And all the time I was hoping that soon they would stop for a breather and then I'd have a chance to catch up.

It was the second Sunday in August and we were making our way to Kiltinan castle for the roundup. The castle was a good three miles from the town. We always made our way there on foot, whether in the fickle furnace heat that sometimes came in August, or the wild windy days you could rely on from October.

My throat was dry, dust-dry. I tortured myself with thoughts of icy spring water from the well at Newbridge, longed to feel it coursing down my throat, numbing my lips, cold as I imagined the North Pole would be. They'd *have* to stop at Newbridge for a drink especially with the sun burning down on us from a bare blue sky.

When, finally, mercifully, they reached Newbridge and stopped I caught up and plunged my head into the ice-cold well water.

Twenty minutes later we were crossing the North Rock, the castle rising into view, tufts of yellow weeds visible on its walls in the sunlight. Mrs. La Terriere would be moving around the courtyard, dressed in corduroy trousers, a man's cap on her head. She kept a large herd of ponies and horses roaming free and unhindered on the land surrounding the castle. Was adding to the herd all the time. She'd take off from the castle without warning in pony and trap. Sweep happily along the narrow roads that twisted and wound through the countryside around the castle. On her way to look at another pony or piebald. Sometimes selling, more often buying. It was doubtful that she ever counted the same number of horses at consecutive roundups.

There was great excitement in rounding up the herd, guiding it into the stable yard for Mrs. La Terriere's inspection. But it wasn't love of horses or ponies that drew us to Kiltinan for those occasional Sunday roundups.

It was the place itself, the castle and the buildings around it. Every pathway enticing, mysterious.

The past seemed to cling like moss or lichen to its stones and walls, its multitude of gnarled, ancient trees. You could feel the past and ghosts of the past everywhere, unseen but present. The mustiness of long centuries could be smelt in the mortar of its old walls and ruins. I would not have been astonished to see a troop of Cromwell's Roundheads come clattering up the avenue. Wandering round Kiltinan castle was to wander in the calm country of another age.

We crossed the North Rock, the old ruined church away to our right.

The mother had told me that she used to meet the father at that old ruin when she worked as a maid in the castle. He would cycle out from the town to meet her. I pictured her, slipping up through the yard in the quiet of the evening, wheeling her bike past the cowhouse. Probably excited, the two of them, her sneaking up, him waiting, wondering, in the shadow of the old church. Then the sudden surge of delight and relief on seeing each other. A quick greeting then off on their bikes to a platform or a dance.

We were coming the opposite way to her clandestine route, down past the arched openings of the cowhouse, the yard covered in dried green scabs of cowdung.

We cut across the stable-yard and out under a high archway fitted with crooked wooden doors that were only ever closed when the ponies were brought in.

Seeing a crowd gathered on the gravel sweep in front of the castle banished the tiredness of our three-mile journey on foot. Mrs. La Terriere moved stiffly about in her corduroys chatting. Prodding at things with a brass-tipped walking stick. I gazed at her man's clothing: her body coat, her cap. And wondered why. I'd never seen a woman wearing trousers before. And wouldn't until much later, when women began to wear slacks.

231

Suddenly a clatter of hooves and shouts came from the direction of the avenue that led from the road gate to the castle. The Carew girls had arrived, four of them, cantering along, whooping, staging a dramatic arrival to take part in the roundup. They always arrived like that on their ponies, making them rear and wheel as we looked on like peasants. They were constantly in motion, trotting, cantering, ponies sweating, shaking their heads, always leaving their droppings in a trail, never given time to drop them in a pile. I was fascinated by the girls and the ease with which they handled their ponies. Almost how I imagined Apaches would do it. And the American tee shirts that they wore. Bright red, yellow, blue. I'd only ever seen those in films. And their blond hair, flying wildly behind them as they galloped. There was something wild and unfettered about them. They were so completely absorbed in their private world of ponies that they didn't take a moment's notice of us. We may as well have been invisible. They came from a different world, the horsey world. They cantered past us, around us, even through us. There was an irresistible glamour, an unpredictability, a heedless air of abandonment and polite superiority about them that we would never possess. Would never seek to possess.

'Just 'cos they're riding aul' ponies they think they can look down on us,' Jim said.

I didn't think the Carew girls would stop what they were doing if the sergeant, or Virgilius, or the parish priest should come along. Would not be as deferential towards them as we always were. I envied them their self-belief, but sensed that such confidence would not come as freely to us.

Hugh O'Donnell from somewhere near Thorny Bridge had come to help too. Mounted on his big, hairy-hoofed, cob with short legs and a barrel of a stomach. His tail matted with pieces of briar, streeling along the ground behind him. Hugh's thin legs were encased in a pair of wellingtons. Because of the length of his legs his irons were unbelievably long giving him a comical appearance. The cob was wall-eyed and wild with flaring nostrils and took an unrelenting hold that had Hugh almost standing in his

232

stirrups.

'Howya Mrs. La, great day for the roundup Mrs. La,' he shouted.

Mrs. La eyed the cob, the length of Hugh's irons, shook her head and walked away.

The herd was grazing east of the castle. Sliabhnamon, looming in the background, seemed almost within touching distance, the patchwork of green hedged fields on its lower slopes gradually merging into a vast, brown and purple expanse. A sure sign of rain, Mamie Mackey would say. But Mamie was beyond saying anything like that now.

The Range sloped away from the castle and down to the river where the herd was grazing. Some were in the water plashing about, swishing their tails, not suspecting that very soon half a dozen wild pony-riders would be descending on them.

Mrs. La Terriere began organizing the roundup.

We, along with a number of other people on foot, were instructed to form a line that stretched from the gravel sweep out onto the range. Our job was to stand there, wave our arms and huzz the ponies towards the arched doorway.

Hugh and some others were sent to form a line on the hill that overlooked the river to the east. Mrs. La Terriere was anticipating that the herd would head in that direction and wanted them there to turn them back.

'G'wan Hugh,' Judo roared as he rode away.

The girls would have to get behind the herd, cajole and haze them into the funnel that we'd formed.

'Remember girls, take them gently, d'you hear?, gently,' Mrs. La Terriere called to the riders.

They wheeled their ponies round, kicked them into a canter and made away towards the river intending to ride around the herd in a wide loop.

A stallion called Eagle's Nest was the undisputed leader of the herd. He moved about with a prancing, proud, almost contemptuous motion. A kind of declaration of independence directed towards the humans who thought they were his masters.

As soon as he spotted the riders coming he swung away from the river and headed uphill to the east. Mares, foals, piebalds, ponies, half-breds, following in a fan-shape. Hooves drumming, tails streaming. From where we stood we had a view of the horses galloping up along the slope towards the spot where Mrs. La Terriere's Quaker mother was buried. And Hugh was waiting with his co-riders, in a line along the ridge of the hill like Apaches watching a wagon train. The herd swung around behind Eagle's Nest intending to make for the river once more. Finding that they were flanked by the Carews they swept onto the avenue behind Eagle's Nest. They straightened and galloped towards the castle with Hugh and the sisters behind. Eagle's Nest swung towards our line. I prepared for flight.

'Don't let 'em break through,' Hugh roared.

We jumped, screamed, clapped our hands. They veered away, charged onto the gravel sweep, milled about. They calmed a little and eventually let themselves be coaxed and eased through the archway and into the yard with a clattering of hooves. The doors were closed. Inside the ponies shunted and bumped one another. Eagle's Nest pranced, head tilted contemptuously, tail extended, nipped others on the neck and hindquarters. Let nobody get close to him– apart from Mrs. La Terriere. He condescended to her inspecting him from a respectful distance.

'You're a proud devil, right enough,' she said to him, admiringly.

He tossed his mane in agreement.

Mrs. La Terriere would spend about an hour walking through the herd, talking, cajoling, eying them expertly looking for signs of injury or illness.

We slipped out of the yard while the inspection was still going on. Wanting to explore. Leave the girls to their ponies. Anyway, the excitement was all over. It would just be a case of opening the arched doors and letting the ponies charge back onto the range when Mrs. La Terriere was finished.

'C'mon,' Jim said, 'we'll head for the Boiling Pot.'

The Boiling Pot was at the base of the massive rocky eminence

234

on which the castle had been built. We ran to the pathway that wound down around the base of the craggy rock. I paused, looked up along the sheer, impassive width of the castle facing eternally, immovably, east towards Sliabhnamon. Wondered for a second how any rock could support the weight of all that stone laid on stone. How had they built it up from the edge of such a drop?

It was old, so old, so inscrutable, it seemed to me that there must be centuries of secrets hidden behind those opaque windows waiting to be uncovered. Maybe there was one at the end of the pathway we were on. It wound mysteriously down into trees and undergrowth that seemed to strive hopelessly upwards towards the castle rising to a dizzy height above. Giant Scot's pines were dwarfed by the immensity of rock and castle. We ran on lured by the suggestion of secrets, the hope of discovery. From far below came the muted roar of water, intensifying with every downward step. Eventually the path brought us to the place of death, the Boiling Pot, where, it was said, a priest had met his end in the days when Cromwell was in the land.

'He was thrun from way up there,' Jim said, leaning back, pointing up, up, to the top of the castle far above.

It was a long way to fall.

'That's his blood there,' Judo said to me in a hushed voice, as if he was whispering in the church.

He pointed to a large rock in the middle of a pool. There was a rust-coloured mark on it. People said it was a bloodstain. It looked more like rust than blood but I preferred to believe the bloody romance in the story of a priest of the people thrown to his death by Cromwell's men. People had scrubbed the bloodstain away – but it had come back almost immediately.

We stood for a while gazing at the rock, imagining the priest tumbling from the top of the castle. The water boomed and roared from under the rock, rushed through a sluice and onto a wheel that pumped it up to the castle.

We wandered along the rough pathway that ran to the river and came to a suspension bridge, the kind that jungle adventurers would come upon in films, the kind that swung and swayed as you crossed it looking fearfully down at the water below. Except there wasn't much in the way of water in the river below this bridge. The river was wide but shallow and rocky. We ran back and forth along it a few times but soon grew tired and left the gloomy shade of the castle and headed back up the pathway to daylight and the walled garden. The mother had often spoken of the dogs that were buried in the garden with their own headstones. It was a strange notion to us, putting a headstone over a dead dog. Most people that we knew would have found it difficult to put a headstone over their family graves. I read the verse chiselled onto one little headstone:

'And the little ghosts that trot behind us,

Untiring from the past,

May at some golden, glittering gateway,

Find us, and know, 'tis heaven at last.'

The mother had often recited that verse to us. It was written on the headstone of Master Rory's dog, Tommy. Master Rory, Mrs. La's son, had been killed in action during the Second World War in 1944. It seemed sad somehow, standing there in the garden reading the verse and thinking of Master Rory dead on some battlefield with no headstone to his name.

There in the garden we heard calls and the clatter of hooves coming from the yard. The ponies were being freed once more, allowed back onto the range. I pictured them, Eagle's Nest at their head as usual, cantering down the sloping grassland to the river. Free to roam as they pleased once more.

We wandered round the garden. It was mostly a wilderness of shrubs and old vegetable patches with scutch grass. We ate some apples and pears deferring the moment when we would have to face the long trek back home in the heat. Arguments were breaking out and I just wished that we could be magically transported back to our kitchen and supper. Hooves clattered again, more measured, less frantic this time, heading in the direction of the road gate. That would be the Carew sisters heading for home, followed by Hugh O'Donnell on his big cob.

We'd had enough and set off back to town. Strung out and

streeling along the road. Walking westward into the evening sun. The heat intense. We'd have to be back in time for the Sunday evening devotions at seven o'clock.

We'd walked about a mile towards town when the sound of a car came suddenly from behind us. A rare happening. We stopped, waited, hoped it would be someone heading to town. Someone who'd give us a lift. Just this once, maybe. Just to sit into a car and be driven back home would be heaven. Save us the long streel back. It came putt-putting and swaying around the bend at the top of Springmount Hill. And, miraculously, mercifully, stopped when it reached us. It was a big battered grey old Cambridge.

'Jump in, let ye, jump in,' the man behind the wheel called, revving the engine to keep it from cutting out.

'Hard on ye walking in that hate,' the man said.

In between quizzing us as to who we were, our fathers, mothers, that kind of thing.

It turned out he knew all of our relations.

'Tell yeer aul' fella I was asking for him,' he shouted, as we got out.

The trouble was we didn't know who he was.

'Huh, where'll I cash that,' the father said when we told him later on and he'd figured out who the driver of the car had been.

Fifteen minutes later we were sitting on the form in the kitchen, the Angelus ringing as we spread jam on slices of brown bread for our supper.

Telling the mother all about Kiltinan and Mrs. La Terriere. Hoping she wouldn't remember the evening devotions and Benediction.

She did.

# 44

# Johnnyo

Johnnyo was standing there in the doorway. Not wearing a stitch. Body gleaming white and scary in the morning light. Blue, veiny legs. Thing like a white pudding hanging from him. A jug in his hand.

'C'mere to me young fella, c'mere, g'win to yer mother there and get me a sup o' milk to colour me tay,' he said.

He banged the door shut and left me holding a blue-hooped jug without a handle.

Johnnyo lived behind the second door to the right of our house. The paint on the door had faded to an unrecognizable hue. The boards were rotting from the bottom up. Johnnyo had lived alone since his father had died just before the start of the summer holidays.

His father had been an old man – bent almost double when he'd died.

'Sure 'twas time for him to go,' the father had said, when he'd got word of old Dinnyo's death.

I couldn't figure out how it could be time for anyone to die.

'Arrah sure, he was old, the poor divil, and tired, maybe he had enough of the world,' the mother said.

That was another dark thought: that when I got old I'd grow tired of living in the world and want to be dead. Pad Power looked old to me – I wondered if he was longing for his life to end.

After Dinnyo's death, calling to our house with the jug for a sup of milk, or with a bowl for a few grains of sugar, became an habitual thing for Johnnyo.

Johnnyo worked as a drover and usually left the house in the early hours of morning. It was always late, approaching darkness, when he returned. Sometimes he wouldn't come back for days and when he did return wouldn't leave the house for ages.

The door would only open when he wanted some of us to get something for him. Or when a farmer called looking for him to do some droving. Depending on who the farmer was: some went away muttering and shaking their heads after banging fruitlessly on the door.

The mother always felt sorry for Johnnyo – especially after the old man had died. She'd send him out bits and pieces of dinner. Whatever we were having ourselves: spuds mashed with butter, carrots, parsnips mashed together. Rarely meat. It wasn't much. But it was all she could give him.

'God bless your hand ma'am,' Johnnyo would say.

Occasionally he'd come into our kitchen and eat at the table. Sometimes, if she had a little extra money, when we got work thinning beet, or picking apples or spuds, the mother would buy a couple of packets of oxtail soup as a treat for us. She'd always save some for Johnnyo. He'd sit at the table blowing on the soup, slurping it loudly off his spoon.

'That's great stuff ma'am, 'twould put hairs on yer chest, pity about me head, though,' he'd say, winking at me.

His hair was red and wispy and thinning off the top of his head.

He always asked for a saucer when the mother poured him a cup of tea. After he'd put sugar and milk in it he'd tip the tea onto the saucer and suck it up noisily.

The mother would bring him a flaming twist of paper from the fire to light his Woodbine.

'Mind me eyebrows, missus, the hair is scarce enough as it is,' he'd say.

'Amn't I a good-looking fella enough eh?' he'd ask winking at me.

'Sure wouldn't a dead woman rise up on one elbow to have a look at you,' the mother would always say.

'And why wouldn't she now, sure the sight o' me would bring the dead back to life, so 'twould,' Johnnyo would answer, and himself and the mother would laugh.

I was fascinated by Johnnyo and the work he did as a drover. I asked him once what the longest distance was that he'd ever hunted cattle.

'To the county Cork. Near Mitchelstown. For the hungriest aul' hoor of a farmer that ever pulled up a britches,' he said.

'How did you get back home?' I asked.

'I swam,' he said, 'in all the porter I drank in Mitchelstown. Sure they were bad aul' drinking houses in that town, with a rowdy aul' set in most of 'em, 'twas a cowld hoor of town, so it was. Took me three days to get home out of it.'

I wondered how long it would have taken him to get home if he'd liked it.

He paused to slurp tea from the saucer. Coughed and wheezed from his Woodbine.

'Where'd you sleep Johnnyo?' I asked.

'Ditches and hay barns.'

'Were you ever in dread to be out there in the dark of the night?' I asked him.

'In dread o' what? Sure Jaysus the only thing you need ever be in dread of in this world is a Christian in daylight. Sure I was out many a dark night in many a lonely place and I never met anything worse than meself.'

I pictured him out there peering into the darkness all around. Like Geronimo.

'Sure the drink is a great lad to make a fella sleep,' he said.

Sometimes he gave out about the landlord to the mother. Mainly because he'd fallen into arrears with the rent.

'A hungry aul' effer, the same fella wouldn't help a lame dog over a stile,' he said to the mother.

We had the same landlord as Johnnyo and sometimes I'd bring our rent money to him and a little red book that the mother used to keep track of payments. And arrears. There were always arrears to be cleared.

He was a big, red-faced, peevish looking man who leaned on the counter in his shop, glancing at me over his glasses as he entered the amount in a thick ledger. He never spoke to me. Just looked at me with his hard eyes. As if he was putting a value on me. I didn't like him.

I brought Johnnyo his jug of milk and a couple of slices of buttered brown bread.

He was seated on a form at the fireside wearing his trousers now with one strap of his braces pulled up over a bare shoulder, the other dangling.

'Your mother's a dacent woman, an angel sent from heaven,' he said.

The smell of the bucket came thick and heavy from the bedroom. There was little in the way of furniture.

I stood uncertainly not wanting to walk out the door when he was speaking to me.

He balanced the cup of tea on the rim of the tea chest.

'I have to go hunting cattle today, for a hungry aul' hoor up around St. Johnstown, I have to hunt them over towards the county Limerick,' he said.

I said nothing. Just looked at the broken nails on his toes.

'Jaysus, you're full o' talk – is it a balavawn you are or what?' he asked.

'G'wan, shag off with yerself so,' he said, finally.

I went out and sat on the wall at the far side of the road, trying to decide what I'd do for the day. Soon after Johnnyo pulled the door behind him and strode away down The Valley. Rhythmically slapping his cow stick against the leg of his trousers. Measuring off the miles between himself and the county Limerick.

Judo came up The Valley and sat beside me on the wall. We weren't very enthusiastic about doing anything in particular. Our chat was lazy and desultory. Finally we slid off the wall and wandered away to join the rest of the gang at the camp.

When the Angelus bell rang at twelve o'clock we headed home to have lunch.

And stopped short in astonishment when we came in sight of our front door. A black Austin Cambridge was parked opposite our house. Three men were standing outside Johnnyo's. The one wearing a suit looked very important with a sheaf of documents in his hands. The other two were workmen. They had tools: a

241

hammer, and a couple of nailbars. The workmen were trying to force Johnnyo's door open with the bars. It didn't take a lot of forcing. I ran into the kitchen.

'Mammy, Mam, what are they doing at Johnnyo's door, they're trying to break it down?' I shouted.

'Whisht, whisht, that fella in the suit is a bailiff, they're putting Johnnyo out of his house, they're evicting him.'

Evicting him?

'Why are they doing that Mam?'

'Probably 'cos he's in arrears with his rent.'

I remembered the arrears in our rent book.

'But we do be in arrears, Mam, don't we, will they come and put us out on the road too?' I asked, suddenly terrified.

'Of course they won't we always pay the arrears so we do, poor aul' Johnnyo couldn't get the money to pay,' she said.

'But what's Johnnyo going to do, where'll he sleep?'

'He'll find another place, don't worry,' the mother said.

I went outside and joined the rest of the gang, sitting in a row on the wall – watching in silence. The door finally gave way with a cracking, tearing sound. The man in the suit entered the house followed by the workmen, grimfaced and uneasy looking.

Pad Power bobbed his way out from behind his half-door to get a better view of what was going on.

'Them feckers should be ashamed o' themselves, putting a poor man out on the side o' the road. As bad as bloody Cromwell or the Tans, so they are, they'll never see the face o' God,' Pad said.

Mention of Cromwell and the Tans triggered a host of associations from the history that we'd been taught at school. In our minds Cromwell had been the great evictor, even if it had been hundreds of years ago.

A gloomy, resentful air settled around us. It seemed that some terrible wrong was being visited on us. Not just on Johnnyo, on all of us. Nobody spoke after that. The men went about their work in silence.

All of Johnnyo's furniture was dragged out and piled on the

gravelled area between the front door and the edge of the road. The men moved quickly in and out – you could tell they were anxious to get away from there as quickly as possible.

The kitchen table came first, followed by two chairs, the tea chest, a form, a double bed, mattress, pillows, and blankets. There was only one bed. Dinnyo and Johnnyo must have slept together. Just as we did. But we were boys, children. It seemed strange to me that two grown men, father and son, should sleep in the one bed.

A po pot was carried out. The bucket, half full. I'd gagged when I smelled it that morning. A faded picture of the Sacred Heart. Some old clothes and boots. The greasy hat and overcoat that Dinnyo used to wear. The furniture was old, rickety, inadequate. There was nothing that spoke of ease and comfort. All of the things that made up Johnnyo's private world were exposed in the cruel light of day, thrown together in a pitiful pile for our curious eyes to gaze on and wonder at.

It didn't take long to complete the job.

A bolt was fitted and the door padlocked to make sure Johnnyo couldn't get back in. Finally the man in the suit tacked a notice on the door then sat into the Cambridge. The two workmen scrambled quickly into the back and they were gone.

The mother came out with the baby in her arms and stood talking quietly to Pad Power. Gazing sadly at Johnnyo's few belongings. People from further down The Valley came up to wonder at it all and have a look at Johnnyo's worldy goods. They stood around, speaking in hushed voices as though in the presence of a corpse.

That evening it rained heavily. I stood at the front door, watched it kicking up off the road, pouring down on the furniture, saturating Johnnyo's bed and mattress.

Before drifting off to sleep I heard it drumming still on the roof, gushing from the broken downpipe. I wondered where Johnnyo was at that moment, if he was in out of it. Or finding shelter in a barn or a shed somewhere on the road home from the county Limerick. The drink helping him to sleep. Unaware of what would greet him when he got home. Unaware that he no longer had a home.

He didn't get back to The Valley until late on the evening of the following day. The rain had stopped. All of us were in the kitchen when a banging sounded on the front door. It was Johnnyo, banging with his cow stick.

'What's after happening missis, Holy God Almighty what are they after doing to me at all and me few bits o' furniture nearly washed away with the rain? Sure I told the hungry aul' effer I'd fix up with him, if he'd only have patience with me I'd pay him all,' Johnnyo said.

'Twas an awful thing to do, sure you wouldn't do it to a dog,' the mother said gently.

'Sure couldn't he have patience, 'twas hard to manage without the father's pension, that used to keep the rent paid,' he said.

''Tis hard when you get into arrears, 'tis hard to catch up,' the mother said.

Tears slithered down Johnnyo's cheeks.

'Sure what am I gonta to do now, God help me, I dunno what I'm going to do sure I haven't a cousin in the world and not a penny in me pocket.'

He sat there in the kitchen for ages after he'd finished eating, smoking a Woodbine. Usually he didn't delay when he'd finished eating. That evening he sat there uncertainly, calling down curses on the landlord and all his family.

Eventually he stood to go, said he knew a man out beyond Cloneen who might be able to help him out. The mother slipped something to him in the doorway.

'You're an angel from God, missis, an angel from God, sure I'd be hungry only for you,' he said.

''Tis a pity I can't do more,' the mother answered.

When he stepped outside and saw his belongings in a sodden pile he broke down and wept. He thanked the mother again for all her kindnesses to him then set off down The Valley, a forlorn figure fading into the damp twilight.

Twenty long years would pass before I set eyes on Johnnyo

again.

Next morning the parish priest went walking past with barely a glance to spare for Johnnyo's belongings. It didn't seem right, somehow. Johnnyo had been evicted and nobody seemed to care.

Two days later an old woman and her daughter moved into the house while Johnnyo's furniture was still heaped outside. They brought even less with them into the house than Dinnyo and Johnnyo had. On the third day after the eviction a man came one morning and we watched him load the furniture onto a trailer drawn by an ancient tractor. He drove away carrying the last trace of our neighbour Johnnyo.

From that day on I didn't just dislike our landlord, I feared him.

# 45

# Endings

August had begun with endings. Mamie dying was the worst of all. Then Paudie leaving for Youghal. Then it was Horse, not *dying*, of course, but leaving the camp. And leaving us: even though we saw him almost every day, he was still gone from us. So many times when he was tormenting me I'd wished that terrible things would befall Horse. Privately, of course, not aloud: that would have brought terrible retribution on my head. When he had split from us I was surprised to find that I missed him.

'Wouldn't you kinda miss the Horse?' I said one day to Judo.

'For fuck's sake, Jonno, are ya gone in the head, all of a sudden?' Judo answered.

One day, shortly after the roundup at Kiltinan, Horse suddenly stopped being an Indian. Stopped being one of us. Cut us off.

Such a change took place in him. All in the space of a few days. One day he was our chief, a central part of our world, putting on war paint, ordering us around – next he was pedalling past us on his father's bike, wearing a brand new long britches. Still wearing the Elvis slick in his hair. Incommunicado with importance. Gone over to the world of work.

He was now an apprentice projectionist in the Capitol cinema. A few months short of his fourteenth birthday, earning fifteen shillings a week. Wheeling cans of film by handcart from the railway station, heaving the reels onto the big projectors, rewinding them when the films ended, hand carting them back to the station every second night. That was his job. As well as sweeping the floors, cleaning the toilets and shovelling the ashes from the furnace when the cold weather came.

At halftime he'd saunter into the cinema foyer, smoking, standing aloof, making sure we saw him. Every move he made saying, look at me, I'm the sorcerer with the secret knowledge making those images appear on the screen. I'm earning.

His education was complete. There would be no question of secondary school in September. That would have to be paid for. More important things had to come first: food, clothes. Anyway, secondary school was the very last thing that Horse wanted. Like most of us in the gang he would rather have picked hot stones in Hell than go on suffering at the hands of the brothers, learning only to think badly of ourselves.

I really envied him when I heard that he had finished school. It was what I longed for, dreamed of, every day: an end to the daily, paralysing fear that made my mind freeze as I walked along the Rocklow road every morning, slowly making my way to school. Leaving school would end those fearful images of Virgilius that haunted me day and night all through the school year. All that torture would end when I reached that magical age: fourteen. Yes, fourteen was the age to be. And I was only twelve. I would have to spend almost three years in sixth before I reached fourteen. Before I was free. There would be two years in the desks at the back of sixth class. Sitting below the map of Ireland. That's where the lads who couldn't go to secondary marked time until they reached fourteen. In limbo: not fully in the school but still not out of it.

The Patriarchs, Virgy called them.

'We'll consult the Patriarchs,' he would say, sarcastically, when someone was stuck on a sum or a spelling.

On the day Horse began his career as a projectionist Dinny from down the road left for London. Dinny was seventeen. There was just him and his mother.

'Sure he went off to America when the craythur was only a baby, that misfortunate woman never heard of him from that good day to this,' the mother said, once, when I asked where Dinny's father was. I'd thought that maybe he was in London, like so many other fathers.

Dinny had been working for a farmer since leaving school at fourteen. Every morning he'd ride away early to work on an ancient BSA motor bike that he'd inherited from an uncle.

247

Summer and winter evenings you'd hear the slow bass beat of the engine echoing off houses and walls as he came home – a sound I wouldn't be hearing anymore. He'd sold the bike to some fella from Cashel. The money would pay for his journey to London.

Dinny was doing a steady line with Maura Slattery. They were always together, going to the flicks, walking around Jesuits' Walk or down along the riverbank. Maura was going to follow him over as soon as he was sorted out beyond, his mother said.

And as soon as she'd said it she'd be crying and dabbing at her eyes.

'Sure what's here for them, nothing, not a thing,' she'd say.

The night before Dinny went some of the neighbours gathered in Kelly's small kitchen to keep him and his mother company. Judo and I hung around outside listening to the babble of voices. Later songs were sung. Mostly old Irish ballads, the foot-stamping, hand-clapping kind, leavened with the mournful and sad. Buzz Lawrence playing the melodeon.

'That's your aul' wan singing, ain't it?' Judo said.

I listened.

Sure enough the mother was singing 'Will you go Lassie, go?'

Her voice was sad and plaintive in the silence that had fallen. Buzz played softly on the melodeon. Everybody joined with her in the chorus, not raucously though, but low, restrained, as though the poignancy of the song was saying for them what they could not put into words. The ache in the mother's voice as she sang, the slow, quavering notes from the melodeon, filled me with an immense sadness, for her, for Paudie far away in Youghal – for Horse, Dinny and Maura.

For all who had left, for all who were staying.

I waited up for as long as I could, wanting to hear all about it from the mother when she came home. Fiddling at the radio, trying to get it onto Radio Luxembourg, the Station of the Stars. Annoying the father, angry and awkward because he was unaccustomed to being in the house with us when the mother wasn't there.

'Is she going to stay out all bloody night?' he grumbled finally, stalking off to bed.

Sleep got the better of me. I didn't wake fully when she came in, just heard the faint mumble of voices from their bedroom.

Next day Dinny was catching the evening train. It would take him to the boat that would carry him across the Irish sea to Fishguard in Wales. From there he'd catch another train that would have him in Paddington station seven hours later, in the early hours of a London morning.

Judo and I sat out on the wall opposite our house waiting to see him pass on his way to the station.

He came slowly, carrying a small, brown suitcase, looking older than seventeen in a belted overcoat and cap. Face tense. Maura was with him.

'Good luck to ya now Dinny,' Josie Barrett said, from the half-door, 'sure, you'll miss him now, Maura.'

'Ah, sure, indeed, 'twill be grand to get a break from him, grand,' Maura answered, forcing a laugh.

Suddenly though, her face contorted and she was crying.

'Jaysus,' Dinny said.

We followed them as far as Kerry Street cross, then watched as they walked up the Cashel road towards the station house. Looking slight and forlorn, the two of them, walking away from us in the soft light of that summer evening. Dinny would probably never come back again. Not to live anyway. He'd maybe come on holidays once in a while, for as long as his mother lived. Then never again.

Judo came with me into our kitchen. We sat around the table turning the pages of our comics. Not saying much. Voices and music humming softly inside the radio.

I pictured the sun slipping behind the jagged rim of the Galtees, and Dinny, probably sitting at a carriage window, seeing long evening shadows stretching across the fields and hills of his home place. Tense, wondering what lay ahead at the end of those train journeys.

Then came the distant wail of the train whistle. Like the desolate screech of a banshee. Echoing long, mournfully, fading,

fading, as the train passed through the wood at Grove. Making us pause from our reading. In our mind's eye each one of us seeing the train, in the dying light of evening curve into the tunnel of trees at Grove Wood then disappear beyond the foothills of Sliabhnamon.

Beyond Sliabhnamon everything would be strange to Dinny. A different world.

'Sure that's where ye'll all end up, alannah, in England or America,' the mother said later, when I asked questions about Dinny and his father.

I tried to picture the boat and the sea and the station at Paddington, but couldn't. The furthest I'd ever been from home was that bus trip to the Feis Ceoil in Waterford. And once to Cashel with the mother. Only half-formed images of boats and crowded city streets that were grim, grey and inhospitable came to mind. Absorbed from films, black and white television. Books. Distorted by an erratic imagination.

There was a melancholy air along The Valley for a day or so after Dinny's departure. It was always like that when someone new left. And then people secretly began to wonder who would be next to go.

'Sure, Dinny's poor mother'll miss him now, the craythur,' the mother said, wistfully.

I began to feel that maybe this going to London that I had been fantasising about might not be all that it had seemed.

# 46

# Summer Rain

Big, swollen clouds came crowding in from a seemingly endless queue beyond the Galtees. Soaking the old town and the countryside all around. Water gushed from broken roof gutters. Rushed into storm drains.

Tall roadside weeds drooped. In a field close to the town late-cut swathes of sweet-smelling hay that had been ready for saving sank slowly and were flattened by the weight of their own wetness.

It wasn't good weather for being an Apache.

The porous sacking of our tents was useless in such rain. We sat for a while inside, Judo trying to teach us how to play poker. But the rain seeped through and dripped coldly onto the backs of our necks. Ran down inside our shirts. The ground squelched under out feet.

We retreated indoors, driving the mother insane, waiting for it to clear.

There were occasional breaks in the downpour. The clouds briefly broke apart to taunt us with a fleeting vision of blue sky, bake us with an intense, thundery heat. When thunder did rattle and lightning flash the mother lashed holy water onto us and around the house, made us kneel to say a decade of the Rosary for deliverance.

In the mornings horse's hooves sounded wet and plashy on the street outside. Milk still had to be drawn to the creamery. Distorted through wet windows farmers on their carts looked like ghostly, misshapen monks, wearing cowled sacks to keep the rain off their heads and shoulders.

The Clashawley roared along its bed, yellow and foamy, swirling and swerving, threatening to overflow its channel. When I went there during a break to empty the bucket the contents disappeared instantly. That was one good thing about a flood in the river. You didn't have to look at revolting things floating away on a slow current.

During breaks Pad would lean forlornly on his half-door drawing on his pipe. Gazing up and down a deserted road. Even the dogs had withdrawn.

'Terrible weather for the Redskin,' he called as I sprinted to the Judy for a bucket of water.

'They'll be floods after this, I never seen such rain,' he said, as I passed back.

We had to content ourselves with playing endless games of Beggar My Neighbour and Snap that sometimes developed into bouts of wrestling and pucking. The mother had to wave the sweeping brush over our heads to restore calm.

'I'll blacken me arse and run mad outa this house if that rain don't end soon,' she threatened.

There would be an uneasy silence for a while after that – furtive nudges and pinches were traded, gradually escalating into outright fighting once more until the brush had to be waved again. Then the whole process began once more until the mother had had enough and we were banished to the bedrooms. She didn't respond to the whinings, pleadings and accusations that were directed towards her through the timber partition walls.

Only when the father came home was complete silence achieved.

Eventually the rain cleared and we emerged to a bright, rain-washed world that glistened wetly in watery sunshine. We spent the first day running around to see the wonders wrought during our two days of confinement. A tree branch wedged across the eye of Watergate bridge. With it the rusted frame of a bike carried from somewhere up-river. The wheels of an old pram. Lakes of water had formed in fields. In a low meadow a single haystack stood islanded in the blue sky reflected in surrounding water. It would still be there at Christmas, when the floods were long gone. Swans had appeared. And seagulls. Grass combed flat in hilly fields. A symphony of running, dripping water sounded all around.

Three days passed before our teepees were dry enough for us to go into them once more.

We came and went, came and went to our camp, like wild animals living on the verge of human society leaving and returning to their lairs. Slipping into hedges. A lot of the time we were unseen, left to our own devices. Close by the adults but unseen.

Under their noses.

# 47

# Paudie Comes Home

It was Saturday and we were coming back, Jim and I, from our Legion of Mary paper round.

We'd delivered all the papers but had collected very little money. There were always people in arrears. And always the ones you thought would never be.

The mother always liked to hear about 'the better-off class o' people' who weren't too prompt about paying their bills. With her it was more than just idle curiosity about other people's way of living – the comparisons she made between them and us helped ease the agonies of guilt she felt when we went into arrears on the rent book and at the grocery shop.

And we were often in arrears.

That Saturday morning Jim was already launching into a naming of the day's defaulters as he pushed open the kitchen door.

'Mam, that aul' Mrs. Morgan wan still won't pay her ...' he was saying.

Then stopped dead in mid-sentence.

For there was Paudie at the table. Drinking tea.

Sitting in his usual spot astride the inside form, keeping an eye out the window, as if he'd never been away.

We stood in the middle of the kitchen floor staring at him.

More than four weeks had passed since he'd gone away in Mick Hogan's calf-truck. He had changed. Definitely. He looked much older than fourteen. The hair had grown back, he had it almost in full Beatles' style now. Shining. Probably he was using shampoo now instead of second-hand soapy water. He had on a new, brownish jacket with narrow black lapels and collar, fastened almost to his throat with fabric covered buttons. And a pair of drainpipe trousers without turn-ups. Shoes with pointed toes.

'Jaysus, Paudie, you're all mod,' Jim said.

We slid onto the form opposite, taking a good look at him.

He was pale and a little pimply. The aura of other places hung round him. As if he wasn't *our* Paudie anymore – that some essential part of him was elsewhere. Beyond us.

'For feck's sake what are ye all gawking at?' he said.

We stared even harder when he drew a packet of Carrolls No.1 from his pocket and lit up. I looked at the mother.

'You better not have that thing in your gob when your father comes in,' she said, warning him.

You could tell though that she was pleased to have him home. If only for a short while.

Paudie grimaced.

Silence came down.

'I'm doing the Legion papers now instead of you Paudie,' I said, awkwardly, breaking the silence that was beginning to greaten.

'Never. In for the trip to Tramore Jonno, eh? I bet you feck money from the secret bag.'

'There's never anything in it to feck,' I said.

'He probably has it gone before it gets to you,' Paudie said, tossing Jim's hair.

'Feck off, willya,' Jim said, delighted.

The secret bag was passed round at the Legion's weekly praesidium meeting.

'Don't be putting bad ideas in the child's head now,' the mother said.

'Mrs. Morgan still not paying her arrears, eh – what d'ya think of that Mam?' Paudie said, looking a bit easier in himself.

'She gets *The Universe* and she's *six* weeks behind now,' Jim said, importantly.

Jim took the money and made all the entries in the little red cash book that went with the paper round.

I carried the papers and knocked on the doors.

The mother then said that Mrs. Morgan would often fry a pan of onions and open the windows to let the smell drift out so that the neighbours would think she was frying steak for dinner. When they wouldn't even have a sausage. And her husband a teacher, if you don't mind.

'Full of notions, that one,' she said, emphatically.

She hunted us from the kitchen then saying she had to get the father's dinner that he'd be home soon and here she was gabbing away and nearly forgetting that Saturday was his half-day.

Paudie brought us all over the bridge to Mrs. Shea's shop to buy sweets: slab toffee, sherbets, liquorice strips and Flash bars – then down with us to the river bank for a secret scoff. Just like Billy Bunter's gang at Greyfriars.

We sat on the bank gormandising. Paudie lit up and watched us.

At night, just before sleep, I used to rehearse a million questions that I planned on asking Paudie when he finally came home. Now, as he lay back on the grassy hump blowing smoke-rings for Frank and Gerry, I couldn't think of one. All I could do was gawp at him and wonder why this awkwardness had come between us. Even though I was happy that he was here with us now on the bank of the river.

He seemed a bit uneasy now in our world, this old world of his.

Was a bit broody looking, as if he had things on his mind.

He'd be leaving on Monday, getting a lift back from somebody in Clonmel who worked down in Youghal.

Paddy Harney, appeared, making one of his rare excursions beyond the half-door and along the riverbank. Walking his bowlegged old mongrel on the end of a thick piece of rope.

'Look at this,' Paudie said, taking a box-shaped object from his pocket.

It was a small camera. A Brownie.

He'd bought it cheap from a man who came into the bar every day and wanted money for drink. We were all grabbing for it wanting to look through the lens.

'Hold on, hold on,' Paudie said, 'line up there on the hump and we'll get a snap of ye all.'

He stopped Paddy and took his photo as he stared suspiciously at the camera. Then he showed Paddy what to do and got him to take all of us sitting on a hump on the riverbank. Paudie in his fancy gear, us in our khaki shorts, crepe-soled sandals and sleeveless jumpers.

I went with Paudie when he started back towards the stile. Jim stayed behind showing Frank and Gerry how to skim stones on the water.

Ellie was leaning over her half-door.

'Well, Holy Mother, if it ain't Paudie, sure I thought for a minute 'twas one of them Beatle lads with all the hair you have on yer head now,' she said.

'And look at the style,' she added, scrutinizing him.

'How d'ya get into them yokes at all,' she asked, nodding at Paudie's drainpipes.

They chatted and bantered while I stood listening, savouring every word exchanged.

'Willya smoke a fag?' Paudie asked, drawing the packet of Carrolls Number 1 from his pocket.

'Oh, bedad now, tipped and all, if you don't smile, I suppose I better have one or you'll only be talking about me,' she said.

She smoked and coughed for a while.

'I'd sooner the aul' dudeen,' she said, flicking the butt across the road.

'You'd want to keep clear o' the boss man and his machine or you'll be going back to Cork with only a headful o' skin on you,' she called after Paudie as we left her.

'D'ya want to come to the camp with us Paudie,' I asked.

'Naw, I couldn't be bothered with all that now,' he said.

'Can't ya come and take a photo of the camp?'

'I thought that feckin camp would be gone by now, you stay here, I'm heading down to meet Horse,' he said, walking away.

I was disappointed.

I'd had some kind of expectation that he'd come with me to the camp. That I'd be able to show him off, like a conquering hero. With his mod clothes and his camera. I couldn't believe that he didn't want to see the camp, after all, Horse and he had done most of the work building it. Now it just didn't matter to him anymore. He seemed to have other things troubling him.

Later, when the father had gone off to the betting office for the big cross-channel meetings we all filtered back home as our stomachs dictated. Paudie said that he'd brought us some things. He handed me a book called *Kidnapped*.

'Read that instead of all those aul' comics and Indian books,' he said.

I'd been reading a book called *Indian Wars and Warriors* when he'd left.

Jim got a penknife with six blades. Frank and Gerry got a little box each with Dinky cars.

There was something odd in the way Paudie handed them to us, as if they were mementoes not presents.

Around suppertime the father came home. Carrying a brown bag. He dipped into it and handed each of us a Chester bun.

This was becoming one of those days when everything seems just right.

'You must've had a good day,' the mother said.

'Ah, sure, I only held me own,' he said.

Which was what he always said – win or lose.

'Well Mother o' Jaysus, the pote is back,' he said, reeling theatrically away from Paudie.

'Begor now, we'll have to do something about the length of that mane, won't we Mam,' he added, stirring his tea.

'Leave him alone, he's grand the way he is,' the mother said.

'There's no-one touching my hair,' Paudie said.

'I dunno, now, I dunno, sure 'tis longer than the mane on a tinker's pony,' the father said, winking at me.

Jim saw it too and we laughed to reassure Paudie.

He didn't smile.

On Sunday morning the mother had to call over and over again to get Paudie up for Mass.

'It's all just mumbo jumbo, Mam,' he said.

''Tis only one half an hour, it won't do ya one bit of harm,' she answered.

He came with us to the church gate then walked on past it. During Mass I marvelled at Paudie's daring.

It was a mortal sin, though. If he'd fallen down and died his soul would've been damned for all eternity. Judo and I left just before the final prayer which would only be a venial sin. I'd probably have to spend a couple of hundred years in purgatory if I died soon.

Judo said that missing Mass *wasn't* a mortal sin and that Paudie would be all right.

I decided I'd go to confession on Saturday after the Legion papers – just in case anything should happen to me. I made a quick act of contrition, too, just to be on the safe side.

I wasn't going to risk eternal damnation on the strength of Judo's theology.

That afternoon we went to the camp to listen to *Pick of the Pops* as usual. There was only Jim, myself, Judo, Philly Landy, Pony, Frank and Gerry. A listless air hung over the camp, as if nobody really cared about it anymore. As if there wasn't any real purpose to our being there.

I was distracted, wondering if Paudie would come, make it like old Sundays. I thought about Horse, too – he hadn't come to the camp at all since becoming a trainee projectionist at the cinema. Our leaders had forsaken us.

Even the familiar blast of the intro to *Pick of the Pops* and Freeman's voice booming out didn't rouse us in the way that it used to. We sat back listening, not saying much. The lower reaches of the charts were played off with Freeman's usual dramatic asides. The lower places in the Top Twenty were mostly filled by numbers on the way down, slipping slowly beyond the boundaries of our awareness. Usually there were some new entries heading upwards to the Top Ten. The old ones, unless they were really good, would have become tiresome by the time they'd slipped to the bottom placings of the Top Twenty.

Brenda Lee's quavery voice drifted through the dead air: 'You went travellin,' travellin' but will it last, I wonder, I wonder...' she was singing, singing about pain and separation.

Why did songs always have to be about those things, I wondered.

I wished something happier would come on, something to blow away the peculiar Sunday dreariness that enclosed us like a grey curtain. The hills, sky, trees, the horses in the neighbouring field, the whole world, seemed indifferent. Would always be, it seemed.

When Freeman reached the top five he cranked up the suspense as usual with a big build-up to the top three.

He was introducing the top five, booming it out: Frank Ifield down to fifth spot, The Searchers knocked from the number one spot, now at number two, then finally the number one: 'sitting at number three last week... a young Liverpool lad... no stranger to the charts...or to you pop-pickers... – the opening chords of the song sounded – ... your new number one ...BILLY J. KRAMER... AAAAND... THE DAKOTAS!!!...BAD TO ME!!!!!...

It had been playing on the radio all through the week so we knew some of the words.

'If you ever leave me, I'll be sad and blue/ don't you ever leave me...'

Paudie looked a bit like Billy J. now, with his hair long and getting fairer as it lengthened.

The afternoon ended as drearily as it had begun. Paudie didn't come. And didn't arrive home for his supper either.

I was awakened late by voices from the kitchen. It sounded as if the father was querying Paudie's late arrival home and the cut of him. I lay awake as he pushed into the bed beside me smelling of beer and cigarettes.

'Where did ya go today Paudie, Billy J. Kramer is number one,' I whispered.

'Billy J. Kramer me arse,' he said.

Almost instantly he was asleep.

I didn't know it then but it would be my last sight of Paudie for a very long time.

When I woke up he was gone.

# 48

# The Red Combine

On the Wednesday after Paudie had gone back to Youghal I coaxed Judo into cycling with me to see an abandoned combine harvester on a farm out near the mountain. A couple of miles beyond Kiltinan castle. Beyond the radius of the familiar world that we gallivanted in. The combine had been left there the previous autumn but I'd never been out to see it. Everyone had been talking about it at the time. Mamie had told me that it had run out of diesel half-way through cutting a field of corn. The farmer had simply walked away and left it. Left everything, farm and all.

'Why?' I'd asked.

'Oh, the banks, no doubt. He went a bit haywire after the father and mother died, bought all kinds of machinery. Probably owed piles to the banks,' she'd said.

We'd been idling around the camp, trying to think of fresh things to do when I'd remembered it. I was all excited, full of enthusiasm because I'd never seen a combine harvester before. Had never been beyond the gates of Kiltinan castle. Neither had Judo, but he wasn't too bothered about it.

'C'mon, c'mon willya Judo,' I said, 'we'll go, just the two of us, we'll sneak away on the rest of 'em, it'll be like a secret mission once we get beyond Kiltinan.'

'Secret mission me arse, d'ya think we're commandoes or something?

'Ah c'mon Judo, I'll get the loan of a big bike from Philly Landy, I'll carry you on the bar.'

'On the bar? A commando on the feckin bar of a bike, and the arse cut offa him?'

'*I'll* sit on the bar so, and you can pedal.'

'Sure I'll be killed, trying to carry you and your big arse all the way out there.'

'Ah for feck's sake, Judo, willya come on, willya.'

'Going up all those hills, some mission all right, commandoes

261

cycling to see a shaggin combine.'

I hated having to coax him, but I had one and sixpence in my pocket. I didn't want to spend any of it on Judo but I'd have to tempt him somehow. He agreed finally, when I told him I'd buy some broken biscuits and two bottles of O'Brien's orange at Ned Meagher's so we could have a secret scoff when we got there. And I had to promise him first look after me when I bought *The Dandy* at Bert Newport's the following day.

We set off on a big brute of a man's bike with rusty mudguards and a gammy cotter pin that caused the left pedal to slip from under my foot when pressure was on. It had belonged to Philly Landy's father, before he'd gone off to London to work. Judo's main concern was for the orange and biscuits clamped onto the carrier. The saddle was rock hard and set too high – I knew I'd have a sore feckin arse by the time I got back home. My toes barely reached the pedals. It was hard going, carrying Judo on the bar, him grumbling non-stop, my knee knocking against his left thigh: the bar cutting into his arse. His arse would be sore, but I didn't care. The pedals escaped from me sometimes. And as well as trying to pedal I had to appease him. Constantly coax him along. Say, hold on there Judo it won't be long now 'til we're there. Like talking to a shaggin big baby. His roundy poll knocking against my right cheek and ear.

We had to dismount and walk up even the slightest of hills. When we had struggled to the top of Springmount, the biggest, steepest hill, and could see the top of Kiltinan castle to our left, Judo started to sulk, wanted to sit down and polish off the biscuits and orange. I was tempted but refused – knowing that if we had our scoff there he'd only want to turn back. And anyway, having a scoff on the side of the road wouldn't be much fun. With Judo grumbling we mounted up once more and wobbled onto the downside of Springmount hill.

I pumped my legs, pedalled really hard, built up speed until we were flying downhill in a rush of wind, rattling gearcase, flies bouncing off our faces, ditch blurring by, occasional fleeting, corner of the eye glimpses of animals through gaps: cows, horses in astonished stances as we flashed by.

'For feck's sake,' I shouted, when Judo attempted to take control of the handlebars, making the bike veer suddenly across the road to the right, roadside grass, buachalainns and nettles slapping against my right leg.

'Yippee,' Judo shouted.

'We'll be feckin well killed,' I roared.

'G'wan Jonno, g'wan, keep pedalling, keep pedalling,' he screamed, suddenly elated.

Our impetus and my pedalling carried us past the entrance to Kiltinan castle and less than quarter of the way up the incline beyond before we gradually wobbled and teetered to a stop.

We walked once more, Judo babbling and excited now that we had ventured past our known boundaries.

Finally we came to the farm on gently-sloping land that rose and rose away from us, field after field, farm after farm, until it merged into the lower slopes of Sliabhnamon.

We hid the bike at the entrance and made our way along a rough, potholed avenue spined with a thick green sward dotted with buttercups, dandelions and daisies. Sharp-toothed briars stretched across our path. No-one had travelled along there for some time. Some blackened bales of hay lay in the ditch on one side of the avenue. We moved along on high alert, like soldiers behind enemy lines.

There was strangeness in the air all around us, a sense of solitude. The farmhouse and out-houses weren't any different to those you'd see on any of the farms between here and the mountain. It was the atmosphere. Something like the unnatural quietness that must have hung over Hamelin after all the children had been lured away. A kind of hopelessness. All sounds seemed to be in the distance. Even the crows seemed to have abandoned the trees that surrounded the house and outbuildings. Their cawing sounded remote, faint. We were isolated here in a pocket of silence where all human activity had ceased. Like the enchanted, sleeping land in a fairytale.

A flower-garden with overgrown shrubs, flowerbeds and miniature hedges run wild was railed off at the little-used front side of the dwelling-house. It had probably been a showpiece for the farmer's wife. A haven for her in the evening under the eye of Sliabhnamon.

I'd often seen her in town for second Mass on Sunday. In a pony and trap. Patient pony tethered to the railing outside the

Abbey church.

How many spring and summer evenings had she spent there in the one spot on the farm given over to unprofitable things? Weeding, tidying. Her work in the kitchen over for the day. Away from the morbid silences of the house. Her husband had been famous for his pipe-smoking silences. It wasn't hard to imagine her ghostly presence lingering there. I wondered what she would have thought if she could see the deserted farm, and the abandoned combine rusting in the field. It mattered little now – she was gone to join her pipe-smoking husband in the silence of the grave.

The little flower-garden, her sweet-scented haven from the drudgery of farm-work, had become a wilderness without her loving hands to nurse it. But still putting out beautiful blooms in the midst of a forest of weeds.

In the yard behind the house a horse's boxcart without wheels lay rotting, its shafts hidden under the creeping edge of a vast dungheap. An old tractor with mowing bar attached had been driven halfway under the arch of the cowhouse. Judo sat on the metal seat, turned the ignition. Moved the gear stick, tried to turn the steering wheel. Both front tyres were flat. Swallows skimmed past us, black blurs, banking and twisting, like fighter planes in a dogfight. Low to the ground, then suddenly curving upwards.

Tar barrels stood under downpipes catching the water that ran off the roof.

There were no farm animals to be seen. Once a foxy wild cat came streaking from a rusted tar barrel.

In the fields rabbits and young graziers scuttled into ditches at our approach, ditches that were slowly advancing onto grassland. A long-legged hare ran lazily through thistles and buachalainns, paused, sat, gazed at us, then lobbed away through a gap and into the next field. As though he'd decided we were no threat but not to be trusted.

Suddenly we saw it in the next field. Towering above a ditch: big, bulky, ugly. A monstrous red leviathan. Abandoned like a tank or guns on a World War II battlefield it stood there massive and forlorn. We stood and looked at it. The machine that we'd seen thrashing corn in Andy Donovan's yard last September had needed a team of men to keep it going. But this combine was so big, bigger than any machine I'd ever seen before. Enormous tyres stll inflated. Standing in a half-cut field of last year's corn. Dead, blackened stalks and grain intertwined with weeds.

'C'mon,' Judo said.

I clambered up a short ladder to the driver's nest. Red, with a mound of blackened corn on the platform under the pipe where ten-stone bags were filled, tied and released down a chute to the stubbles. The rotted remnants of a sack clung to the mouth of the pipe. Bags lay around the field like scattered bodies, corn spilling like guts from holes gnawed by rats. I wondered what could have been in the farmer's head as he strode past those bags of corn all those months ago. Leaving everything behind.

Crows and seagulls circled above. I fiddled with the controls for a while. A stultifying sense of desolation and abandonment pervaded those fields, seeped into my very bones.

'Hey, Jonno, look over there.'

I followed Judo's pointing finger.

Two fields away I could see two men with dogs on leads. Greyhounds.

One groped around in a sack, pulled a rabbit out.

'They're going to give the greyhounds a kill,' Judo said.

We watched.

The rabbit was released and lurched stupidly about for a while, disorientated.

'Run puss, run, g'wan,' I heard one man shout.

The rabbit gathered itself then and took off running, erratically. A greyhound was released. Within seconds the rabbit was being tossed about.

I turned away.

Suddenly I wanted to be gone from that spirit-sapping spot in the shadow of Sliabhnamon. It was too eerily detached from everything, speaking only of decay and abandonment, the death of dreams. The red combine had lost its allure. Better to face the long cycle back than to stay any longer in such a lifeless place.

'C'mon Judo,' I said, 'let's feck off outa here, we'll go and have our scoff somewhere else.'

Judo didn't have to be asked a second time.

# 49

# Ferretting With The Father

We'd come to the end of August.

'I think we could nearly start ferreting again,' the father said one evening.

Start wringing a few bob outa that hungry Corkman, he added.

Cronin, the Corkman, drove around in a little red scut truck buying rabbits and foxes. He was a miserly skinflint who'd take every single rabbit in his purple paws, scrutinise it for defects. And always manage to find some.

Selling him rabbits and the odd snared fox provided us with a few shillings now and again that helped the mother keep us all fed and clothed.

'Oh, ye pissed that fella, so ye did, sure ye burst the bladder when ye were gutting him,' he'd say, peering into the empty carcass, sniffing it with his drippy, needle of a nose.

'You could poke a thorn outa yer thumb with that shaggin nose of his,' the father had said once.

'Sure the mate is no good to me at all now, 'tis spoilt, all I'll have outa him is the pelt,' he'd say.

The father had warned us about breaking the bladder, had shown us how to gut a rabbit properly.

'I'm telling ye now, that effer is tighter than e'er a farmer, 'tis against his religion to part with money, so mind how ye do it,' the father said.

We'd become expert at gutting and were always careful not to break the bladder.

If Cronin couldn't find anything wrong inside the carcass he'd examine the fur, look closely round the eyes and head.

'Faith, that wan had a touch o' the mixey,' he'd say, and cut us again, while we stood there silently cursing him.

'Don't be blackguarding them young lads on me, give 'em a fair price now let you,' the mother said to him one Monday.

'Begor now ma'am, as God is me judge, I wouldn't blackguard the childer for love or money, sure I'd only love to be giving them the full price, but sure what can I do, I have to make a living,' Cronin answered, contritely.

And continued with his docking.

We had no choice but to sell to him – if Cronin didn't take the rabbits there would be no point in ferreting. But he was cute enough not to dock too much, which would've ended his supply of healthy rabbits.

And he always called at around twelve o'clock on Mondays, a day when the few extra shillings from our Saturday or Sunday of ferreting would be welcomed by the mother.

So, on the last Sunday morning of the holidays we planned to set off with the father after first Mass in the Parish church. Most Sundays had a drowsy, languorous feel to them, men hanging around not doing much, keeping their good clothes clean. Maybe going to the pub, and the toss school after the two o'clock closing. Or to a match in the field.

On that Sunday we were on our toes with excitement, eager to get going, watching the father top his duck egg, willing him to eat it up quickly instead of pausing and squinting sideways at the racing page of the paper over the rim of his teacup.

On the road finally we pedalled along in the father's slipstream, anticipating the rituals of the day, each with his appointed task. Anxious to do it right for the father. Wanting to impress him, thrill with delight when he'd say, 'good lad, good lad, fair play to ya.'

Praise was hard-earned, rarely given.

Each of us had something to carry. Along the bar of the bike I had the field nets rolled around the hazel rods and bound with binding twine. I was carrying Frank on the bar as well. He complained constantly that the bar was numbing his arse. I was behind all the way, struggling to keep up.

Shouting at the others to hold on would have been a waste of time.

On the bar of his bike Jim had a spade, the ferreting iron and

Joe. Hanging from the handlebars was a message bag with a flask of sweetened tea and buttered brown bread wrapped in brown paper for our lunch.

The father had Gerry on the bar of his bike and the ferrets in their box strapped onto the carrier. Ugly, sparsely-coated creatures they were: one lemon-coloured with albino eyes, the other turf-coloured: constantly weaving and twisting, snuffling eagerly against the wire mesh on the door of their box. Sensing that something was about to happen, keyed up and ready for action. Their unfeeling red eyes had the merciless look of the killer. No wonder rabbits fled from them in terror. I could never take to them in the way that I'd taken to the terriers and gundogs that we'd had from time to time. I hated when it was my turn to feed them, hated the way they'd raise their serpent heads and challenge me with those red, unblinking eyes.

The father had their bells and a razor blade for gutting in his top pocket.

We didn't cycle far. Out the Grove road we pedalled until we were on the brow of Wood Hill. Down we went in one long falling freewheel, veering sharply left three-quarters of the way down, sweeping through the entrance to Grove estate with a rattle of gearcases and mudguards.

'Aw, Jaysus, me arse, me feckin arse,' Frank squealed, as we bumped along the rutted, gravelly passage until we came to a hump-backed bridge not far from Grove House. At the far side of the bridge we dismounted, and the lads who were on the bars of the bikes hobbled and twisted around, trying to relieve the numbness in their arses.

We left our bikes in a pile against a white, rusting railing that separated a vast lawn from rolling parkland bisected by the Clashawley river. Gathering the gear we set off along the bank of the river, leaving Grove House at our backs, silent and aloof in the motionless Sunday morning air. The grassland along the riverbank was wide, sweeping, unfenced, dotted with shady elm and chestnut. Branches curved long and low almost to the ground. Summer-fat horses and big, sleek bullocks raised their heads as we passed along the riverbank. All days and times the same to them. We glimpsed an otter, a ghostly dark shape vanishing in a blur under the riverbank. A panicked waterhen fluttered noisily across the water seeking cover in the rushes.

There was nothing furtive about our mission, as when we'd netted the river. No need to worry about the gamekeeper when it came to rabbits – farmers and estate owners were always glad of anything that would keep the rabbit population down.

'Where are we going, Daddy?' Gerry called, 'I'm fed up with all this walking.'

'Howld yer whisht will ya, we're nearly there,' he said.

The father led us on purposefully, veering away from the river, through gateways with yellow clay rutted and rock-hard underfoot, along cattle tracks that wound through buchalainns and thistles, running to seed now as the summer neared its end. Flies lifted off cow-pads as we passed. We followed trustingly. He knew the location of every rabbit burrow and warren in the countryside all around the town.

At last we stopped near a high-banked ditch with mature ash and elm spaced along the top. Their leaves beginning to turn. Ancient whitethorn, gnarled, twisted, misshapen, leaning away from the west, filled the spaces between.

'We'll get plenty here,' the father said.

We walked with him as he inspected the clay bank which was dotted with burrows on both sides. He dispatched Jim and me to left and right of the warren in search of the bolt-holes that were always located some distance from the main burrows. A few yards beyond these we set up the field nets. On both sides of the bank. Each net extended about thirty feet out from the bank at right angles. The father took off his body coat and placed it in the space where the field nets abutted either side of the ditch. Rabbits running along the ditch would shy away from it and run into the nets. Once the ferret flushed the rabbits out their chances of escape were slim.

When the father knotted a bell round the neck of the albino ferret I began to tense up, became totally concentrated, in a few minutes rabbits would be racing from the burrows and into the field nets. We'd have to be ready to pounce. The ferrets hadn't been fed since the day before to give them an appetite for the hunt. Not that ferrets ever lacked an appetite for hunting rabbits.

He brought the ferret to the most used burrow to give him a scent of the rabbits.

I watched the ferret squirm and twist trying to escape from the father's hand. He couldn't wait to get underground. The father brought him to the most distant bolt-hole and released him. In an instant he was gone. He'd work his way back through the network of burrows driving the terror-stricken rabbits before him.

Any moment now they'd flee from him into the open air. We stood in a line between the field nets, tense, listening, watching for rabbits breaking from the warren, ready to turn them into the field nets. The father moved slowly along the bank stooped towards the burrows. He paused occasionally, listening intently for the tinkle of the bell that helped him mark the ferret's progress. Suddenly, from where I stood a faint and frantic rumble could be heard: the rabbits had caught the scent of the ferret, were fleeing for their lives through the burrows. Suddenly one then another broke from the warren heading for the open fields then veered along the ditch when we shouted, clapped and waved our arms. Became entangled in the field net. Jim caught the first one quickly, held it by its hind legs – a quick twist and pull on its head and it was dispatched. I got the other one. No matter how many times I pulled and twisted I felt guilty. I'd never gotten used to doing it, I'd just learned to turn it all off, steel myself, and do it quickly, mechanically.

The commotion from the far side told us that rabbits were bolting there too. Soon we had eight rabbits lying on the grass, there would be no gutting until we had cleared the warren. When the ferret was about three-quarter ways through the warren the high-pitched, terrifying cry of a stricken rabbit came from beneath the ground.

'That yalla bastard,' the father swore.

He marked the spot.

The ferret had made a kill.

He wouldn't do any more hunting.

I ran to the father with the ferreting bar and spade.

He listened, one hand raised for silence.

'Nothing, the little effer is lying-in,' he said.

He thrust the bar repeatedly into the bank trying to locate the run of the burrow. He thrust and thrust until finally the bar rattled loosely in the earth. He'd found it. Digging down around the bar until he came to the burrow he followed it along to where the ferret was curled up, sated and asleep, beside a dead rabbit.

'Be gutting them rabbits, and study yeerselves now mind, if ye piss them ye know what the story'll be with that hungry effer from Cork,' the father said.

Jim and I started gutting, another job we hated doing but did as quickly as possible, carefully slitting each carcass from ribcage to pelvis, hooking the horrible, stringy guts out in one movement, scattering them across the field for the scawl-crows to feed on.

He finished out the warren with the other ferret. At the end we had fifteen rabbit carcasses lying on the grass.

We sat on the bank then, squinting in the weak sunshine, drinking our sweetened tea, scoffing our brown bread, watching the scawl-crows swoop on the scattered innards.

'Look,' said the father.

Away towards the river a crane was hoisting itself slowly off the water. An ungainly creature, legs spindly and long, dangling awkwardly, taking ages to get airborne. Following the course of the river downstream, hunting for trout or eels.

The father said he'd probably come back here with the lamp and uncle Mick's lurcher towards the end of October when the nights were dark. It's a great place for rabbits he said, they'll be plenty more of them here by then, the feckers are always breeding.

'Sure they thought the mixey'd kill them off, so they did. No good though, the worst thing that was ever done, bringing in the mixey,' the father said.

Sometimes you'd see a mixey rabbit staggering around the

271

fields its eyes horribly blinded. If we could catch them we'd give them the twist and pull to put them out of their agony.

We strung the carcasses along the length of an ash stick and left them hanging while we moved on to another ditch a couple of fields away. We repeated the operation there and had thirty rabbits at the end of our ferreting expedition.

Each bike had to carry ten rabbits back to town and you had to be careful that they didn't get caught up in the spokes of the wheel.

The damage would only give Cronin another excuse to cut our money.

It had been a good day's ferreting. The father whistled as we walked up Wood Hill, the trees on our left echoing to the evening song of the birds. He wasn't bothered by the grey-bellied carcasses swinging from the handlebars; he'd probably killed hundreds of rabbits between ferreting, lamping and shooting. I wasn't that bothered either, although there was something pitiful about dead rabbits. I was detached from those once-living things now though, like a butcher from a piece of meat. All that bothered me was how much we'd get for them. What kind of tricks Cronin would use to escape paying us the full amount. But one way or another there would be a little extra money in the house. The mother might even rise to buying a sweetcake, or a packet of Mikado biscuits, something that rarely happened. Our afternoon's work and thirty dead rabbits had given us possibilities. I pedalled on, slowly, under the added weight of the rabbits, tired from all the walking and weak with hunger.

But the journey home was always good. Thinking of what lay ahead after supper: sitting on the bridge with Judo and the gang watching cinemagoers cross to the Capitol. Listening to the comments of the men marking time there. Watching them drift slowly away to the pubs.

But there was an eerie stillness coming into these late-summer evenings and darkness was gathering more quickly, driving us home earlier and earlier to the kitchen and our library books and the sound of the radio.

# 50

# Summer's End

Summer's end came slowly, inevitably. I had been pushing thoughts of it away. Not wanting to dwell on endings. But the truth was the life and the energy had begun to seep from the summer.

On that day in June when I'd sprinted across the schoolyard to freedom with a hundred or so other boys summer had seemed a vast store of inexhaustible days stretching away to distant September. But that store of days had run deceptively by.

We were on the threshold of autumn, of transformation, leaves yellowing, summer's sap sinking, its light fading. In Grove Wood hazel trees were bowing under the weight of nuts almost ready to be cracked; sloes and haws were beginning to show in roadside hedgerows.

Hunting horses were being brought in to McCarthy's stable-yard across the river in preparation for the autumn cub hunting season. Those cubs had to be scattered, driven away from the vixen and the familiar home den. Forced to find their own way.

The summer of freedom in faraway fields was over for those horses. They were back now to being stabled, saddled, ridden, kicked along to where they might not wish to go. Just like us.

Soon we'd be back in our plot where we'd endured the icy winds of March. Without Paudie, though. Soon we would have to dig a pit, line it with straw, dig out what remained of the potatoes that we'd planted in pigdung in March, store them in the pit for the winter.

Still, I strove to make that summer go on and on. But I was trying to force something from it that was no longer there. The pain of summer's ending came as much from clinging on to what was almost gone as it did from seeing it end.

All through that last week of the holidays I lay in bed at night tussling with terrifying images that reared up in my imagination: Brother Virgilius in his black gown, pacing between desk-rows, bamboo cane in his right hand, caressing the gleaming, knobby length of it with his left. Awaiting an opportunity to take revenge for the incident with Fritz. I saw the almost demented look on his face, heard the sickening whirr of the cane cutting through the air as he brought it down six times on my aching hands.

I wished I was fourteen, could leave school, end the terror forever.

But there would be no escape.

One evening a tall farmer in an Austin Cambridge called to our house. Looking for apple-pickers in his orchard at College out beyond Kiltinan Castle. We jumped at the chance to earn some money during the last few days before school re-opened. Most of it would be given to our mother. That didn't bother me, I knew she'd give me back the price of the pictures. And that was all I wanted.

He picked us up early in the chill of a dewy morning, drove out to his farm as thin patches of autumn mist drifted across Sliabhnamon, dun-coloured and heathery now in the falling of the year. The autumn air was cold on my bare legs as we entered the orchard carrying heavy plastic buckets, the tree-bark damp and slimy. Droplets showered down on us as we positioned the ladders among the branches. The autumn sun sneaked slowly out after midday to warm us.

We picked from eight until six and were paid seven and six a day.

As we drove home at the end of the last day's picking the sound of the Beatles burst suddenly from the car radio.

'She loves you yeah, yeah, yeah,' they sang, frantically.

It was their latest single, straight in at number one. The sound electrified me, made me sit upright in the car, forget my tiredness. I'd never heard anything like it before, it was so new, so wild, so exciting. Lifting the end of summer lethargy that seemed to have crept over everything.

But the farmer turned it down so low I could barely hear it.

'For Jaysus sake, I dunno how ye listen to that kinda shite at all, 'tis only noise, all that screeching and roaring would give you a pain in yer head, in yer arse even. Tis a wonder ye've e'er an ear left at all. And the long hair on them fellas, like feckin women, so they are. No, give me the Clancys and a good aul' ballad any day of the week. Or Count John McCormack, now there's a man could sing a song.'

For one glorious, wishful moment I saw myself a matador plunging an imaginary sword deep into the back of his thick, bullish neck.

'Did ye know the Pope made him a Count?' he asked, lighting a Gold Flake as the big old Cambridge swung and swayed erratically along the road.

I didn't know, didn't care.

He drove along past Kiltinan Castle coughing and spluttering, spitting out the window, reminiscing about house dances and penny hops, platforms and Mick Del playing at dances in the Town Hall.

When all I wanted was for him to just stop talking and give us the Beatles at full blast. I couldn't wait for *Pick of the Pops* to come on Sunday when I'd be able to hear it in peace.

In the evenings we were tired and bickered around a smoky fire at the camp.

'Are ye still going to that feckin camp,' Horse called to us one evening after supper, with a smirk that said I'm gone from all that kid's stuff now, so I am, I have important work to do, I'm a trainee projectionist over at the cinema and I'm going to be showing the big picture tonight.

The mother was trying to get us to think of school.

'Ye'll have to root out yeer bags and dust the cobwebs off, get yeer pencils and copies together,' she kept saying.

But none of us moved to do it.

'Do ye know, there's not going to be anymore passenger trains coming to the railway station after the ninth,' the mother said one evening.

It took a minute for that to sink in past the distraction of the

Desperate Dan story I was reading in *The Dandy*.

Then I realised that the three-twenty passenger train wouldn't be whistling through Grove Wood anymore, letting me know that school was almost over for another day. I watched and listened for it every schoolday afternoon from my seat near the window. Always, always willing it to appear, wondering would that whistle ever sound my liberation.

One morning the postman brought a registered letter with an English stamp. The mother stared and stared at Paudie's handwriting on the envelope. Almost afraid to open it.

'What in God's name is he after doing?' she said, mostly to herself.

He was in London, working in a bar. In the West End. Getting good money. There were some English banknotes folded in with the letter.

'Maybe he'll meet Spikey in the West End, Mam,' I said.

'Wouldn't he be well away with it, now, meeting the like o' that fella,' she said.

I imagined Paudie in the West End, or maybe walking along Carnaby Street. Our Paudie. On Carnaby Street. I had to re-imagine his location, substitute my sketchy, *Pathe News* images of London for those I had conjured of him in Youghal by the sea.

And it seemed to me then that I was coming to more than just the end of summer, that there was more ending than just the holidays, more happening than simply arriving at a date when school would re-open and summer would really be over. It was more than just one thing ending and another beginning: summer giving way to autumn, holidays to school.

Something was passing that would not be coming round again.

I thought of Paudie so far away in a strange city. Sure, he would be back sometime, but he would never again be part of our lives in the way that he had been at the start of summer. That Paudie was gone forever. Maybe that was why the mother had been so sad when he'd left home and gone to Youghal. She'd known.

I thought of Spikey. And all of the other people who'd gone

away and hadn't come back.

And Mamie, my great and true friend Mamie – spring, summer, it didn't matter how many seasons and new days came and went, they would not bring her back.

Next summer I would be past thirteen, my schooldays all but over, would have to start thinking about earning. There would be no more Indian camps, no playing at being Apaches, no running wild through the wood. We would not be gallivanting again, Judo and I, along the river or out to Kiltinan, wherever our fancy happened to take us.

Summers would come again but never in the same way.

My life was slowly vanishing into the shadows of the past where ghosts were gathering that would later come to haunt me.

Late on the last Sunday evening before school re-opened, after our day ferreting with the father, the gang gathered at the camp. Lit a fire. Sat around trying to re-capture the early summer feeling. But we couldn't. Too much had changed.

With us we had some rags and paraffin oil that we'd bought at Jimmy's in Kerry Street. Finally, reluctantly, we stood to do what we'd come to do. Forming a circle round the teepees, bows in hand, we tied the rags to arrows, dipped them in the paraffin, lit them, drew the strings of our bows. At a signal from Jim we loosed our flaming arrows into the teepees. In silence watched them burn. It didn't take long. The fire took quickly because the sacking was old and dry. Soon our camp was an inferno, flames licking high towards the sky, sparks streaming away to their end in the darkness above. When it had burned down we turned the log-ends in and walked away leaving them to burn out.

Next day we returned to school. Soon I was back in the daily routine of terror.

On the evening of the ninth of September the mother led us out of the kitchen and down to the bottom of our garden. From there we could see the long earthen embankment that carried trains from the overhead bridge at Kerry Street across low-lying ground to the channel that had been blasted through solid limestone at Moanbeg. The sun was sinking away to the west and the dark bulk of the embankment was outlined against piled, pink-shot clouds and salmon-coloured sky.

'Tis there Mam,' I shouted as the sound of squealing brakes came to us through the twilight. I pictured the station platform and wondered if there was anyone getting off. Or on. Maybe someone was boarding the train, bound for London or Liverpool. Leaving the old town behind.

At about nine twenty-five the slow measured pant of the engine sounded, quickening, quickening, quickening as the last train came swaying out onto the embankment, a dark silhouette with lighted windows, gathering speed, rhythmically, going away, away. Stupidly we waved even though no-one could see us. We stood there in silence, the mother with the baby on her hip, the rest of us keeping close to her.

'Wait 'till we hear the whistle, Mam,' Jim said.

The last whistle came to us like a long goodbye, a mournful deathcry, and faded into silence as the train rumbled off through Grove Wood and on into the blackening countryside beyond. We went inside still keeping close to the mother because in the half-light familiar things were taking on strange shapes.

After that my thoughts turned away from summer. I began to look forward instead as the days darkened into October and trees were swept bare of leaves, the countryside drained of colour. There would be long nights ahead in the kitchen, cold, with just the radio humming and comics or library books to read. I began to think of Halloween, and of Christmas in the distance, a shining beacon of bright light in the bareness of mid-winter. And, further away, beyond distant horizons, there was the promise of other, different, summers.

Yes, there would always be something to look forward to. And look back on. Life, it seemed was to be all about endings.

And beginnings.

Lightning Source UK Ltd.
Milton Keynes UK
UKOW02f0624140815

256935UK00002B/26/P